SURGEON'S STORY

Surgeon's Story

Kelly -
Many Thanks -

Mark Oristano
with Kristine Guleserian, MD

Surgeon's Story
By Mark Oristano
1. MED085000 MEDICAL / Surgery / General
2. MED085070 MEDICAL / Surgery / Transplant
3. MED069000 MEDICAL / Pediatrics

ISBN (Paperback): 978-1-935953-77-7
ISBN (Hard cover): 978-1-935953-78-4

Cover design by Lewis Agrell

Printed in the United States of America

Authority Publishing
11230 Gold Express Dr. #310-413
Gold River, CA 95670
800-877-1097
www.AuthorityPublishing.com

Also by MARK ORISTANO

A SPORTSCASTER'S GUIDE TO WATCHING FOOTBALL

DEDICATION

To everyone who works with children.
M.O.

To my family for their unconditional love and support,
for making me laugh along the way, for teaching me kindness,
generosity, and humility. "Dream the Impossible Dream."
K.J.G.

ACKNOWLEDGEMENTS

Thanks to Dr. Kristine Guleserian for agreeing to, and participating in, this project.

To my wife Lynn for all the missed dinners and crazy hours.

To Christopher Durovich, CEO, Children's Health for his encouragement.

To everybody at Children's Health, Dallas for their dedication and talent.

(Unless otherwise noted, all photographs are by the author.)

CONTENTS

INTRODUCTION

by Mark Oristano

To see a human heart beating inside a chest is astonishing. I'd seen it once before in the OR, from a distance, standing behind the anesthesiologist at the head of the operating table. This was my first time observing a heart transplant. A teenage boy's diseased heart had just been placed in a small dish and put aside for later study by pathologists.

I always walk carefully in the OR because I'm terrified of tripping over something, or getting in somebody's way and screwing up the operation. I walked over to the dish slowly, carefully. I got my first close look at a human heart only inches away.

And it moved.

It beat.

The heart didn't want to die. It was trying to pump blood that wasn't there around the body to which it was no longer attached. It pulsed about once every 30 seconds for the next ten minutes, before resting forever.

The heart deserves respect.

* * *

March, 2010

I was finishing up my weekly Tuesday afternoon volunteer shift at Children's Medical Center in Dallas when Dr. Kristine Guleserian, pediatric heart surgeon, stopped me in the hallway. Dr. G, as she is known to everyone, is five feet tall, but "diminutive" isn't a term to apply to her. A thick head of dark brown hair, falling in waves over her white lab coat, frames sharp, probing eyes and highlights the features of her Armenian heritage. Her speech has an insistence that compels you to listen.

"We're transplanting today at four. It's going to be an interesting one. You might want to come and observe."

So, a quick text to my wife to tell her I'd miss dinner, then a change into surgical scrubs, followed by some food to prep for a long evening. (Come on! If you were offered a chance to watch a heart transplant, wouldn't you go?) Four hours later, things were starting to heat up in Operating Room 6. The organ procurement team arrived back at Love Field and immediately called the OR. They had the donor heart in a bright red cooler and were headed to the hospital.

Dr. G invited me to observe the transplant because we were working on a project—this book. When I proposed a book project to her she agreed, though reluctantly. When she tells you that what she does as a pediatric heart surgeon is nothing special, just her job, it's not some egocentric attempt to deflect glory—it's the way she really feels. Several publishers expressed interest in her story, but only if written in Dr. G's first-person voice. That was out of the question, whether written by herself or by me as her ghostwriter. She didn't want her work presented in the first person—too egotistical. Also, her numerous articles in medical journals notwithstanding, she's a surgeon, not a writer. Anybody who loves children and baseball as much as Dr. Guleserian does deserves to have her story told.

Respecting Dr. Guleserian's position, and in order to avoid misinterpreting any of her thoughts on important matters or difficult cases, I decided to present this material in an unusual format. All the comments in italics in this book are direct quotes from Dr. G, taken from transcripts of the many interviews I conducted with her from 2009 to 2016. Keeping in mind the saying that, "Jargon is the professional's conspiracy against the layman," I have added occasional parenthetical definitions to Dr. G's comments. And because I didn't want to tell such a personal story in a dry, third-person way, the first-person voice here is mine, as I relate the story of the amazing people I met, and the things I saw, in my journey through Dr. G's world of pediatric heart surgery. Any inaccuracies in any portion of this book are solely my responsibility.

In some cases, names have been changed for patient privacy reasons. Rylynn, Andrea, and Gilly Riojas, Andrew Madden and his mother, Lauri Wemmer, are the real names of real people, and I thank them for being so willing to share their amazing stories. Some of the quotes attributed to Andrea are taken from the blog she kept during her daughter Rylynn's hospital ordeal. Also, even though the well-known medical facility in Dallas where these events took place is now called Children's Health, I have chosen to use the traditional name, Children's Medical Center, because that was the institution's name at the time Dr. Guleserian tackled the cases highlighted here.

And now, as you prepare to shadow Dr. G, I have two words of advice: comfortable shoes.

Mark Oristano
Dallas, TX

FOREWORD

by Cara Statham Serber

How do you thank the person who literally saved your child's life? What do you say to the woman who held your child's heart in her hands, while your child was kept alive by a bypass machine? Our miraculous time with Dr. Guleserian was so short that I was never able to convey the depth of my gratitude.

Our six-year-old daughter Libby had a cancerous kidney removed at Children's Medical Center on a Friday morning. Before she was discharged the following Friday, the doctors performed a CT-scan to get a baseline for her upcoming chemo treatments. And that scan showed tumors in Libby's heart. They explained that part of the tumor broke off and went from the kidney through a vein to the vena cava and then to her heart. If it got into her pulmonary artery from there, it could be fatal. Just one week after her kidney was removed, she faced another major surgery.

We met Dr. G early on the morning of Libby's open-heart surgery and she put us at ease immediately with her immensely kind and caring manner, explaining her plan for the procedure. She let us know that someone would be phoning us from the operating room with updates. A short time later, we watched in disbelief as they rolled our daughter, so tiny in the grownup-sized gurney, down the hall and into surgery.

Over the next few hours we waited, receiving the promised updates. "Incision has been made..." "Libby is now on the bypass machine, taking over the function of her heart and lungs..." "Libby is doing well..." and finally, "Dr. G has completed the surgery and will meet with you shortly."

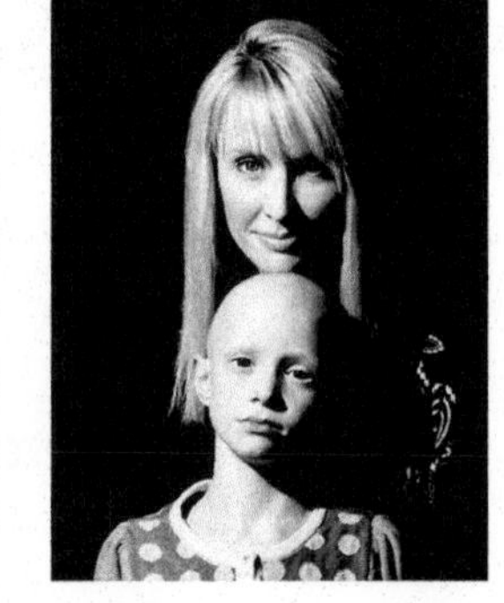

Dr. G. met us in a tiny consultation room and told us the surgery had gone as well as it possibly could have. All of the tumor matter was removed from Libby's heart and pulmonary arteries. Dr. G answered our many questions. We hugged and thanked her and she modestly accepted our gratitude, saying she was grateful to have helped. And then she was gone.

We spent a mere fifteen minutes with the woman who saved our child's life. And it is because of that short time spent with her that I am so thrilled to write this foreword. Dr. G will see in print, indelibly, what an impact she made on our family. She views it as just doing her job. We want her to know what a miracle she is to every family that is fortunate enough to have her take care of their child. "Thank you" alone will never suffice.

Cara Statham Serber
Flower Mound, TX
June, 2016

CHAPTER ONE

A Day in the Life

"We eat stress like M&Ms in here."

OR-5
Children's Medical Center, Dallas
November 5, 2009

Eleven-month-old Claudia lies sedated on the operating table in OR-5, as still as a doll with no moving parts. She looks smaller than her charted weight of nine kilos (20 pounds). Nurses cover her with sterile blue surgical drapes so all that's visible is a 4-inch square patch of skin on her chest. Bright white lights bathe the center of the table. Doctors and nurses in gowns, caps, and masks crowd around. They look almost identical. Except for the earrings. The earrings are the "tell." That's how you know it's her.

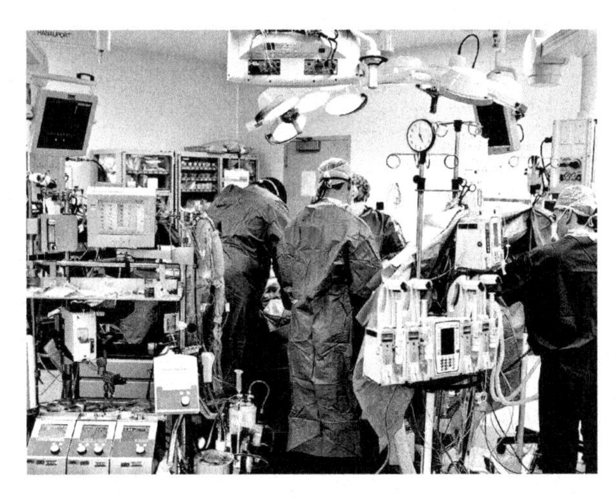

Kristine Guleserian, pediatric cardiothoracic surgeon, is scrubbed in. Dr. G is one of only nine women in the U.S. who is sub-specialty board certified by the American Board of Thoracic Surgery to do what she's about to do—take a scalpel sharper than a dozen razors, cut through Claudia's skin, saw open her breastbone, and spread her ribcage apart in order to repair congenital defects threatening a malformed heart the size of a walnut. It's just after 9:00 AM. Claudia will be in OR-5 until 2:00 PM, along with a team of talented surgeons, nurses, techs, anesthesiologists, perfusionists and others.

Dr. G is in charge.

* * *

Two weeks before Claudia's surgery I had a 1:30 PM meeting with Dr. G at her office. At 1:25, I sat in the waiting room. At 1:30, Dr. G came through at her favorite speed—full. She headed for the door while putting on her white, starched lab coat over surgical scrubs and said, "Come on." We trotted down the hospital hallway.

"This is my world. You wanted to see it. Welcome to my life."

"Where are we going?" I was struggling to keep up with her even though I'm a foot taller.

"We have to do a consult."

"We?"

"I have to. You'll watch."

We whisked past the main desk of the echocardiography lab. Dr. G motioned to the charge nurse.

"He's with me."

We squeezed into the cramped, dark echo lab, where there's barely enough space for the two women sitting at the monitors. Dr. G introduced me to cardiologists Dr. Catherine Ikemba and Dr. Reenu Eapen, and then turned her focus to the echo monitors. An echocardiogram is a moving image produced by sound waves directed at the heart and reflected back again as the waves pass from one type of tissue to another.

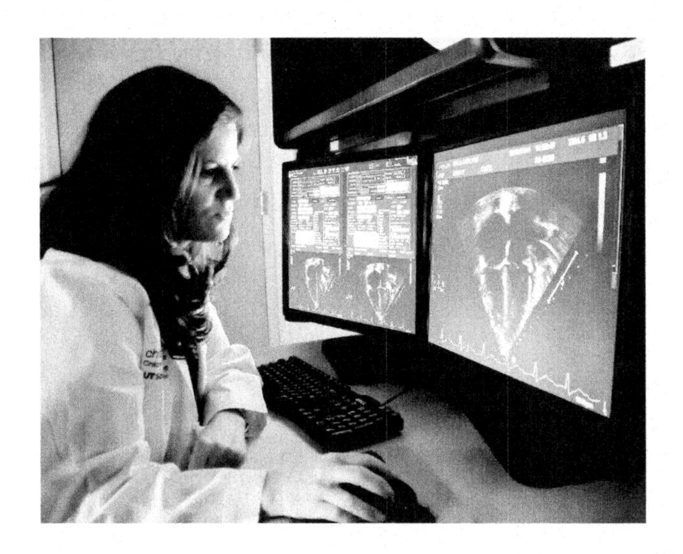

To me it looked like a blurry, moving x-ray. To the eyes of these three doctors it was an intimate cardiac road map. A nine-year old boy had a malformed aorta, and the cardiologists wanted Dr. G's opinion. She was Socratic, asking questions she likely already knew the answers to, saying, "Well, there are several ways to approach this. I might do..." and then asking her colleagues for their opinions.

Two weeks later, I came back for the first of many long days as her shadow. I wasn't quite Alice in Wonderland, but the feeling of falling down a hole did occur to me.

7:30 AM – Heart Center Research Meeting

There's more to being a surgeon than surgery. This day begins in a windowless media room, the kind of video-meeting-training center you'd find in any school or business. Rows of desks and chairs give it a classroom feel. A/V equipment hangs from the ceiling and a large video screen dominates the front of the room. The dress code is strictly medical, no business attire here. Doctors and nurses in scrubs and lab coats shuffle into the room, many with the ubiquitous cup of Starbucks in hand. Today will feature a presentation of two ongoing cardiac studies being conducted at the Children's Medical Center's Heart Center. The room is very cold, and Dr. G wears a black turtleneck dress under her white lab coat. She pulls the sweater neck up over her nose and mouth as the meeting goes on, seeking warmth. A presenter advances to the lectern, and the unmistakable look of a PowerPoint presentation flashes on the screen behind her. The title slide reads:

CHROMOSOMAL COPY NUMBERS IN
HYPOPLASTIC LEFT HEART SYNDROME

I had begun my own rudimentary study of congenital heart disease (heart defects present at birth) before I ventured into Dr. G's world, trying to find a map through the maze of childhood cardiac abnormalities. I knew hypoplastic left heart syndrome (HLHS) was a life-threatening cardiac deformity where the left ventricle, which pumps blood to the aorta and then around the body, is so severely underdeveloped that without surgical intervention any newborn suffering from it will likely die. The pediatric heart specialists in the meeting room critique what they've heard when the presentation ends. A senior physician might question the validity of this or that portion of the research methodology. These are works in progress, not ready for publication. Ongoing study is a part of the physician's job description.

In the meeting room, the media screen glows again.

ECHOCARDIOGRAPHIC PREDICTION OF SPONTANEOUS
CLOSURE OF DUCTUS
ARTERIOSUS IN PREMATURE INFANTS

After only two weeks shadowing Dr. G, I was able to make some sense of this title. The Heart Center team is using echocardiography to predict whether the ductus arteriosus in the hearts of premature infants will close properly after birth, sparing the need for heart surgery. I decided I had to dig deeper into the textbooks to learn more about what was beating beneath my own breastbone.

* * *

The muscle that is the human heart is a four-chambered pump, designed to send deoxygenated blood to the lungs to get a new supply of oxygen, and then send the oxygen-enriched blood on its journey around the body to nourish organs and tissues. The left and right sides of the heart each have two chambers: an atrium on top, and a slightly larger ventricle on the bottom. Each side is like Dali's version of an hourglass. The atria and the ventricles are each separated by a muscular wall called a septum. The ventricular septum is slightly thicker than the septum for the smaller atria.

NORMAL HEART
(VIEWED FROM THE FRONT)

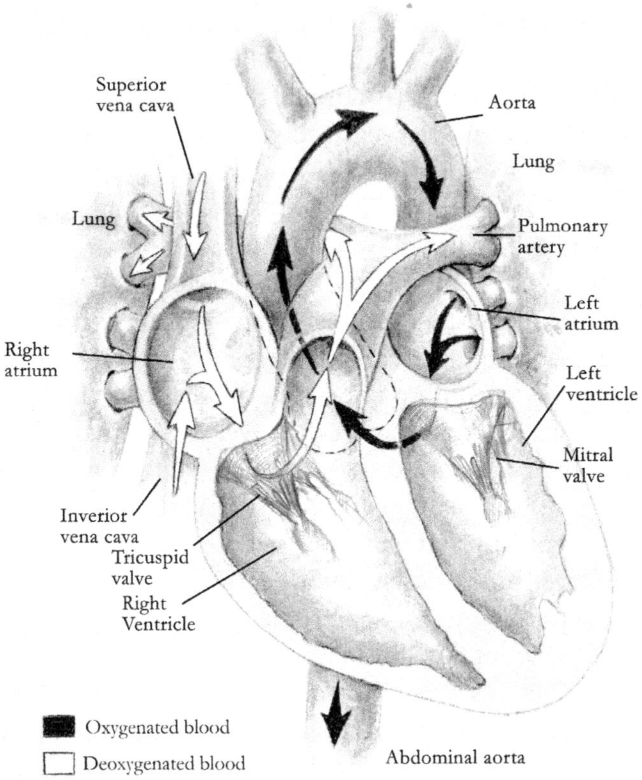

Superior vena cava
Aorta
Lung
Lung
Pulmonary artery
Left atrium
Right atrium
Left ventricle
Mitral valve
Inverior vena cava
Tricuspid valve
Right Ventricle
Oxygenated blood
Deoxygenated blood
Abdominal aorta

(Illustration by Rebekah Dodson)

In a normal heart, deoxygenated (blue) blood enters the right atrium from large blood vessels called the vena cavae, which bring blood back from the rest of the body after distributing oxygen. The right atrium contracts, opening the tricuspid valve, and blood flows down into the larger right ventricle. The contraction of the right ventricle sends blood through the pulmonary valve to the pulmonary arteries, and into the lungs for oxygenation. The newly oxygenated blood enters the left atrium through the pulmonary veins. When the left atrium contracts, blood is sent through the mitral valve into the left ventricle. The left ventricle contracts, blood moves through the aortic valve into the aorta, and off to oxygenate the rest of the body—the brain, the coronary arteries of the heart itself, deep into the internal organs, and superficially to the skin. Over and over again, on average 100,000 times per day. That's an anatomically correct heart. (Anatomic trivia: The pulmonary arteries are the only arteries that carry deoxygenated blood, while the pulmonary veins are the only veins that carry oxygenated blood. Otherwise, oxygenated blood typically flows through arteries, and deoxygenated blood through veins.)

Heart disease in adults is usually acquired. When we develop a heart condition in later life, it's most often our own doing. Smoking, obesity, hypertension, high cholesterol, poor diet, lack of exercise, diabetes, genetics and more contribute to the atherosclerotic disease, heart attacks, strokes and other events that make heart disease the leading cause of death in most developed countries. The number of things that can go wrong with the human heart is staggering. Each year, approximately 40,000 newborns in the U.S. are born with some form of congenital heart disease, although many of them show no symptoms, and problems don't surface until years later, if ever. Since infants haven't had a chance to do much damage to themselves it's fair to wonder how a newborn heart can have so many problems. Congenital heart defects occur because of abnormalities in normal fetal heart development. Fetal lungs are non-functional, because the fetus gets its oxygen from the mother through the umbilical cord. The developing fetal heart contains a series of shunts, like miniature bypass circuits, to direct blood away from the pulmonary arteries and lungs so that blood flow is kept low, and the tiny lungs won't be overtaxed. The shunts in the fetal heart are:

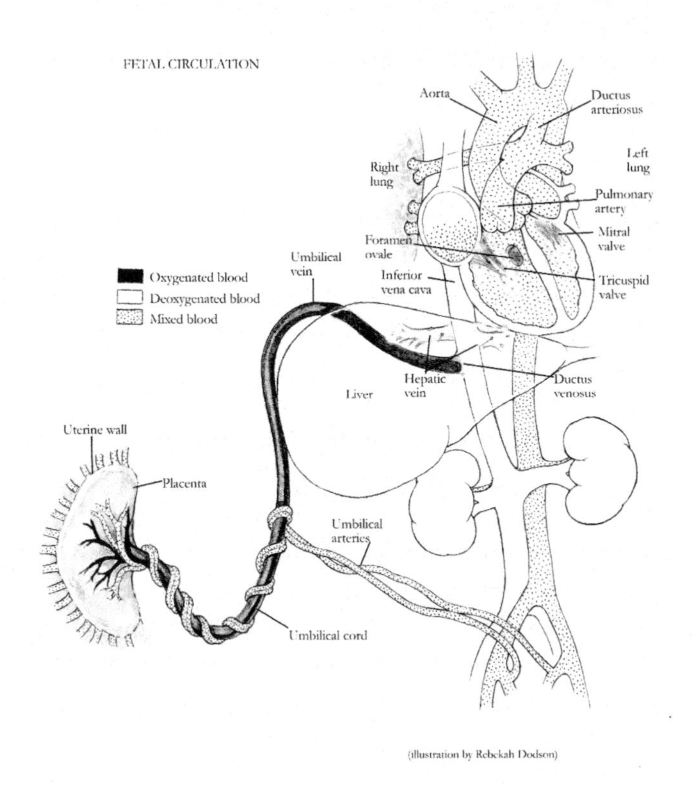

(illustration by Rebekah Dodson)

1. the foramen ovale, which lets blood flow from the right to the left atrium,
2. the ductus venosus, which draws umbilical blood away from the fetal lungs and into the vena cava, and
3. the ductus arteriosus, which connects the pulmonary artery to the descending aorta, thus allowing most blood from the right ventricle to bypass the non-functional fetal lungs.

All three of the shunts are pre-programmed to disappear after birth to create the normal heart design. (The ductus venosus closes becoming the ligamentum venosum; the ductus arteriosus closes becoming the ligamentum arteriosum; and the foramen ovale closes to create an intact atrial septum.) When something interferes with the natural process of newborn heart development it can manifest in hundreds of ways. In certain situations, it's never even noticed.

Cardiac Anatomy 101 is over. Feel free to bookmark these diagrams and return PRN (as needed.)

8:15 AM
3rd floor Cardiovascular Intensive Care Unit

The Cardiovascular Intensive Care Unit (CVICU) has twenty rooms arcing around a large central desk. The furnishings are modern and austere. The pulse of the CVICU is the rhythm of the beeping sound common to every TV medical drama. Each patient is attached to a monitor measuring blood-oxygen saturation (sats), heart rate, blood pressure, respiratory rate, temperature, and more. Each monitor is a computer, producing different sounds for different reasons, the one constant being an audible beep, one for each heartbeat. An infant's tiny heart beats significantly faster than an adult's, so the pace of the beeping is rapid, and each baby here suffers from a potentially fatal malfunction of that rapidly beating heart.

Nurses move everywhere, monitoring every child. Intravenous (IV) fluid pumps hang at each bed—six, eight, sometimes more. One patient has ten IV drips, each one delivering a different life-supporting medication—sedation, painkillers, antibiotics, anticoagulants, blood products, nutrition and others. The drips hang from poles and flow directly into the tiny patient's arm or leg or, more often, into a catheter inserted into the chest for easy access. All these babies are critically ill, critically tiny, many premature. Most of them are smaller than the stuffed animals that sit, unnoticed, next to them.

Another familiar sight from TV medical shows is on display here: the long, white coat, the peacock feathers of physicians and surgeons. Children's Medical Center is a teaching hospital, part of the University of Texas Southwestern Medical School in Dallas. Doctors long past their residencies and now specialists in their fields wear the long, white lab coat. Medical students and interns are in shorter coats. Dr. G is the shortest of the long coat-clad. She's only five feet tall, but as they say in the sports world, she plays six-two. She's not the only woman in the group, but she's the only one wearing a long white coat. The young doctors listen to her.

Heart surgeons, ICU doctors (intensivists), cardiologists, nurses, nurse practitioners, physician assistants, fellows, residents, respiratory therapists, interpreters, social workers, clinical techs, medical students and visiting observers start at one end of the unit and move, room by room, around the floor. A cardiology fellow pushes the computer-on-wheels (COW), and presents each case. This young doctor has made several of the basic choices his career path requires. He's just finished his pediatrics residency, where he worked in various specialties. He's chosen medicine over surgery, pediatrics over adult medicine, and cardiology over other disciplines, making pediatric cardiology his career choice. He's taking his first steps down the six-year road it will take to earn "attending" status, when he'll be in charge of cases. He'll then be a pediatric cardiologist, a doctor who treats young people with heart disease. He'll refer cases needing surgery to people like Dr. G, a pediatric cardiothoracic surgeon. Her career path was twice as long, requiring twelve years to attending status. Cardiologists diagnose—cardiothoracic surgeons repair.

Even though he's out of residency, this doctor is still learning the cardiology ropes. He stops in front of the door to the first patient room and runs down the important events from overnight: vital signs, patient status, complications, and planned treatment. The male attendings ask questions that are pointed and occasionally harsh. Dr. G draws the younger doctors out with her questions, gently nudging them back on the right track. "I didn't hear anything about left atrial pressure there," she tells the presenter, who immediately refers to the COW screen and spews a series of numbers out in a specific order. The young doctor's voice has tensed, rising a bit, as he makes up for his omission. It's unlikely he'll make this mistake again. Terms like "open-chest" and "life-threatening event" are heard on cardiac rounds, said calmly and with nonchalance. Hospital personnel in critical-care settings have to appear outwardly detached. It's a key to staying focused.

The CVICU nurses rounding with the doctors make notes while answering questions concerning how patients fared overnight. There is a pecking order among medical personnel, and some doctors treat nurses as underlings; nevertheless, a tremendous level of trust exists between the doctors and nurses at Children's. If the doctors are the officers of this army, the nurses are the sergeants, the ones who make sure everything gets done.

While the rest of the group moves along the hallway, Dr. G stops to look inside the room of the patient just presented. If she sees a family member inside, and they're awake at this early hour, she goes in to say hello and ask how things are going, to see if they have any questions or need something. She feels a responsibility toward every family, even if she isn't their surgeon. It's not done for effect or because her medical training requires it. This is the way she treats everybody. It doesn't matter if your child has a serious heart condition. It doesn't even matter if you have a child. From the security guards to the hospital CEO, when Dr. G sees you, in the hallway, in the cafeteria, in the OR, she says hello.

Rounds end, leaving just enough time to dash up to the eighth-floor cardiology ward and check on patients who are out of ICU, waiting to be discharged. One young heart transplant patient with pulmonary hypertension has turned down her oxygen level without the nurses knowing about it. Dr. G tells the 13-year-old girl, in a firm, motherly way, that medical decisions are made by the pros and here's how we'll manage the oxygen for the remainder of your stay. She turns the level back up and tells the patient, "You'll get out of here faster. Trust me." The girl nods.

The moments after rounds, before the next issue presents itself, offer a chance to head down to the first-floor food court for a snack. Dr. G's pager beeps as she stands in the cashier's line. She checks the number and heads up to the third-floor office suite she shares with her partners and staff. She phones the person who paged her and, in a flash, it's out the door and back to the echo lab, a half-eaten banana left behind on her desk.

Two weeks after my first visit to the echo lab, I was back. I stood to the side again, this time better able to make sense of some of what Dr. G and the cardiologists discussed as they looked at the screen. Eleven-month-old Claudia's diagnosis was tetralogy of Fallot (TOF), a defect resulting in four different cardiac abnormalities:

1. Ventricular septal defect (VSD) — a hole in the wall between the two ventricles;
2. Overriding aorta — the aorta is not positioned properly on the heart;
3. Right ventricular outflow tract obstruction — for any of several possible reasons, the blood flow to the lungs is restricted, leading to;
4. Right ventricular hypertrophy (which physicians pronounce "hy-PER-tro-phy") —a dangerous buildup of the right ventricle's musculature.

"It's all really one problem," Dr. G explains to me as she looks at the screen. "It's underdevelopment of what's called the infundibular septum, which leads to the other abnormalities."

Claudia has alarming episodes of cyanosis where her lips, fingers and toes turn blue because her oxygen saturation level becomes dangerously low. She also has what are called "Tet spells," when her oxygen level drops so low that her skin not only turns a dusky blue, but she loses consciousness. The preoperative finding of most concern to Dr. G is the extremely small pulmonary valve, the one-way valve between the right ventricle and the pulmonary arteries, which led to expected findings of the significantly thickened muscle bundle below the valve, and the large, misaligned ventricular septal defect.

Thirty minutes later we were walking down a second-floor hallway toward the operating rooms. Dr. G walked quickly, straight ahead, focused. She was getting her game-face on.

10:30 AM
OR 5

Claudia lay motionless on the table in the center of the OR, her head sticking through a hole in the draping around her neck, visible to the anesthesiologists standing at the head of the table. They're concerned with the numerous gauges, medicines, inhalation gases and monitors at their fingertips. They're also in charge of tilting the table at the surgeon's request, to put the patient at a more favorable angle, because the motorized table can be raised, lowered and tilted to various angles at the touch of a button.

(Example of pediatric cardiothoracic humor—A flight attendant goes on the p.a. and asks if there's a pediatric cardiac anesthesiologist on the plane. There is one, in the rear of coach. He signals the attendant and asks what the trouble is. "We have a pediatric heart surgeon in first class who wants his tray table lowered.")

The scrub tech stands at the opposite end of the table, facing a series of trays that hold an array of odd-looking tools: forceps for picking up or grasping things; scalpels that slice through human flesh as if it were air; sutures (thread) finer than human hair, attached to small needles curved like fish hooks.

The scrub tech is the surgeon's right hand, responsible for pulling instruments and supplies for the operation, knowing what the order of the operation is, and arranging everything in the most efficient format for this particular surgery and this particular surgeon. Dr. G knows that when she calls for an instrument, the proper one will be there in a flash. Often, it will be offered to her before she has to make the call.

A six-foot-by-six-foot metal frame sits to one side of the operating table, a cluster of gauges, canisters, and clear plastic hoses. This is the cardiopulmonary bypass machine—the Pump.

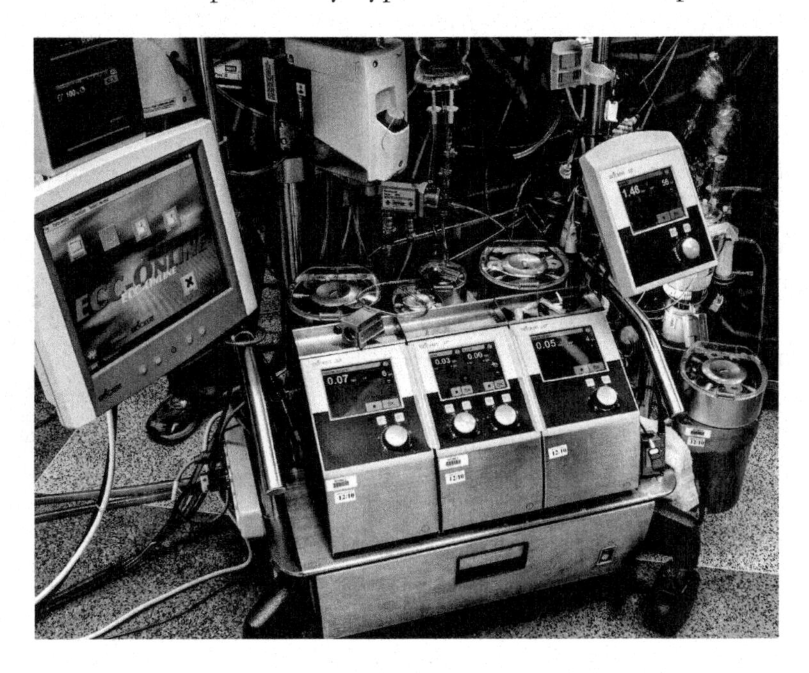

This technology will serve as Claudia's circulatory system so that her heart can be stopped for repairs. Developed in the 1950s, modern bypass machines still use hoses much like the beer keg tubing in the first experimental models. The perfusionist, the specialist in charge of operating the pump, sits at the machine.

The small patch of Claudia's chest that's visible is covered with a material called Ioban, an adhesive membrane coated with iodine. This will reduce the risk of infection when Dr. G makes the initial incision to begin correcting the defects caused by tetralogy of Fallot. Medical knowledge sometimes progresses slowly. Tetralogy of Fallot was first primitively described in 1672. Two hundred years later Etienne-Louis Arthur Fallot, a French physician, described the clinical pathology of the condition. The first surgical treatment for TOF wasn't available until the late 1940s. Dr. G, ever the teacher, drew a diagram of the surgery for me before she scrubbed in.

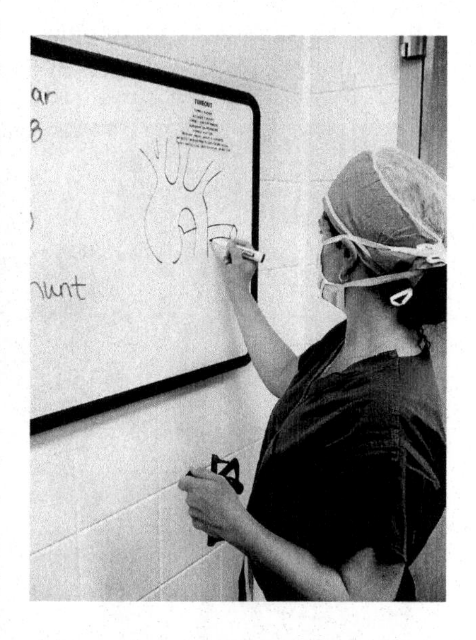

After scrubbing, Dr. G re-enters the OR with hands and forearms still wet. She dries with sterile towels provided by a scrub tech, who then helps her into a surgical gown and gloves. She wears loupes secured over her cap. They look like small telescopes growing from each eye, and they give her a magnified view of the tiny area in which she's working. A fiber-optic cable runs up her back, over the top of her cap and into an intense, bright white lighting instrument/video camera at her forehead, to light and televise what she sees to monitors hung around the OR. Dr. G is at the center of the sterile area, where only those who scrub in can go. The rest of us, wearing surgical masks and caps in addition to our scrubs, have to stay away from the table. She climbs up on a small step stool to get her five-foot frame high enough above the table to work easily, without making her taller assistants bend over.

She takes a scalpel and makes a four-centimeter incision (a mini-sternotomy) in Claudia's chest. Next, she cuts the breastbone open with a small saw and puts retractors in place to hold the ribs apart. The first object Dr. G encounters inside Claudia's chest is the thymus gland, a small, flesh-colored organ. The thymus is an important component of the fetal immune system, but it's not as important postnatally. It gets in the way of open-heart surgery, and since you can live without it, the gland is removed and discarded.

Dr. G takes an electronic scalpel called a "Bovie," which cauterizes as it moves through tissue, keeping bleeding to a minimum. She cuts the pericardium, the sac-like fibrous membrane containing fluid that lubricates the heart. The pericardium has extra meaning for Claudia. Dr. G precisely excises a small portion of the sac and places it in a dish containing 0.6% glutaraldehyde, a preservative fluid. She'll use this patch later to close the hole between the ventricles that failed to seal itself properly before birth. She works around the small space filled with tiny body parts, freeing up the aorta and the pulmonary arteries from the underlying tissue. Claudia has been given heparin, an anticoagulant, so that her blood doesn't clot when it goes through the bypass pump. Dr. G inserts cannulae, small tubes, into the aorta and the vena cavae. The other ends of these tubes are attached to the pump, connecting to Claudia's circulatory system. Because Claudia has very small blood vessels, the work is delicate and precise and the tubes they need for this bypass, like the vessels in Claudia's chest, are extremely narrow. Her cannulae are smaller than the width of a ballpoint pen.

The mood in the OR shifts at various moments. Dr. G had been casually introducing me to the OR team while routine work is going on—as routine as heart surgery can be. But when the cutting starts, the room goes quiet. Dr. G hovers over the small body on the table, staring down into the chest she cut open. The view from the camera attached to her loupes doesn't shake on the OR monitors. She's a human tripod.

The perfusionists are cooling Claudia's body down to 28 degrees Celsius, 82.4 Fahrenheit, to slow her metabolism and protect her heart. Hypothermia decreases the amount of oxygen the brain requires, giving the surgeons time to perform the needed repairs. They aid this chilling process by turning the temperature in the OR down to 64 degrees, so cold that several people drape their shoulders with blankets from a nearby warmer.

Dr. G clamps the aorta, and blood stops flowing to Claudia's heart. Dr. G tells the perfusionists to "Run the plege," short for "cardioplegia," a solution of chemicals inducing cardiac arrest. In order to operate on the heart, they must intentionally cause something that usually kills when it happens on its own. The cardioplegia solution includes potassium chloride, one of the chemicals used in lethal-injection executions. Claudia's heart stops beating and the blood exits her vena cavae into the bypass machine for oxygen, returning to her body through the cannula inserted just above the clamp on the aorta. Her heart and lungs have been turned off. There's no more beeping or EKG activity on her monitor. She has "flat-lined." When the patient goes on pump the heart is like a water balloon with the water let out. It changes in shape from full and throbbing to flat and motionless. The only way to repair Claudia's heart is to stop it, empty it, and then fix it.

The first task is to examine the heart to see if the preoperative diagnosis is correct. The cardiologist on the case has already spent time with Dr. G going over the preoperative echo. It was from this echo that the first surgical roadmap was drawn. But this is a road that can twist and turn without notice. Dr. G uses delicate instruments to retract portions of the tricuspid valve and examine the extent of the defect of the ventricular septum, the wall between the two ventricles. She determines the exact size and shape of the VSD and trims the segment of pericardium she saved earlier in preservative before beginning to sew it in place. Each suture is an intricate dance of fingers and forceps, needle and thread. Dr. G works with a small, hooked needle, grasping it with forceps, inserting the needle through the tissue, releasing and re-gripping with the forceps, pulling the hair-thin suture through, using forceps in her other hand to re-grip the needle again and repeat. The pericardial tissue being sewn onto the ventricular septum has to be secure, and it has to stand up to the pressure of blood pumping through Claudia's heart at the end of the operation.

This isn't like repairing knee ligaments, which can rest without use and heal slowly. Claudia's heart is going to restart at the end of this operation, and whatever has been sewn into it has to hold, and work, the first time. Dr. G find that it's preferable to actually divide some of the chords of the tricuspid valve to better expose the

VSD. After the patch is fully secured, the tricuspid valve chords are stitched back into place.

It doesn't surprise Dr. G when she looks inside Claudia's heart to see that the pulmonary valve is not as she'd hoped based on the pre-op echo. It's malformed with only two flaps where there should be three. She deals with these problems by what she later says is "just putting in a little transannular patch."

Here's what it's like to "just" put a transannular patch on the pulmonary valve of a child as small as Claudia:

First, take a piece of well-cooked elbow macaroni. Tuck it away in a bowl of pasta that has a bit of residual marinara sauce still floating around in it. Take several different-sized knitting needles. Slowly, without damaging the macaroni, insert one of the knitting needles into it to see if you can gauge the width of the macaroni on which you're operating. Then using a delicate, incredibly sharp blade, cut a small hole in the piece of elbow macaroni, maybe a little larger than the height of one of the letters on the page in front of you. Now use pliers to pick up a small needle with thread as fine as human hair in it. Use another pliers to pick up a tiny piece of skin that looks like it was cut from an olive, so thin that light shines through it. Take the needle and sew the olive skin on to the hole you've cut in the piece of macaroni. When you're finished sewing, hook up the piece of macaroni to a comparable-size tube coming from the faucet on the kitchen sink, and see if you can run some water through the macaroni without the patch leaking.

That's the food analogy. Those are the approximate sizes Dr. G worked with as she patched Claudia's pulmonary artery. She made it a little wider to give it a chance to work more efficiently, to transport more blood with no blockage, requiring less work for the built-up heart muscle of the right ventricle so it could return to a more normal size. It wasn't the repair she'd planned to make—she'd wanted to spare the valve, but it was too small and abnormal—however the repair done was the most suitable under the circumstances, and it gave Claudia her best chance.

Before restoring Claudia's natural circulation, allowing the heart to beat on its own again, the team makes certain that no air is in the heart or the tubes from the pump, because it could be pumped up to the brain. Air in the brain can be fatal. When all the repairs are completed, and after the heart is fully de-aired, the aortic cross clamp is removed. Blood flows into the coronary arteries to wash out the cardioplegia, the solution that induced coronary arrest. The heart begins to beat again. Claudia is rewarmed and weaned from the bypass machine.

Claudia's heart starts up on its own, with a strong, normal rhythm. With her heart beating again the beeps and the peaks and valleys on her monitor return. All is well. An echo technician and a cardiologist wheel a portable machine into the OR to perform a transesophageal echo—a more detailed view than the normal, external echo. Everything looks good. Chest drains are inserted to handle post-operative drainage, and temporary pacing wires are stitched to the heart, should anything go wrong with Claudia's heart rate or rhythm during her recovery from surgery. Dr. G draws Claudia's ribcage back together with stainless steel wires, perfectly fastened and tightly tucked down in a figure-of-eight configuration she learned from Dr. Michael Pasque, one of her surgical mentors.

Claudia and the surgical team return to the CVICU, and Dr. G monitors her reentry to the unit, making sure the nurses understand Claudia's condition and the proper procedures to be followed for the next 24 hours. From there, Dr. G enters a small room tucked away from the noise of the unit to meet with the family. Claudia's mother, father, and aunt are waiting. Dr. G sees Mom wiping tears away.

"Are you crying? Oh, no, no need to be crying, everything is fine." Her wide smile reassured Mom, who put away her tissues.

She tells the family what she did, and why she did it, using a serviceable mixture of medical and lay terms.

"The arteries that go to each lung are a little bit small. We'll watch those over time. She'll definitely need to have a pulmonary valve at some point. The hard part is predicting exactly when that will be. Some people go a good portion of their lifetime without needing one, until their 20's or 30's. My brother had this same surgery when he was an infant like Claudia, and he still hasn't had a new valve put in yet. But he will someday."

The simple fact that her brother had similar surgery seems to put the family a little more at ease. They know Dr. G has been on both sides of the equation, and she can relate to their anxiety.

From meeting with the patient family, it was off to a brainstorming session with the architects designing new cardiac surgery suites. They wanted staff input on what should go where, how far the doors should be from the operating tables, etc. In the OR, a matter of a few feet can be the difference between life and death.

Lunch came at 3:30, which can actually be early in Dr. G's world. She debriefed herself from the surgery as we ate, describing to me what had taken place. She would later dictate all this for the official surgery report in medical terms such as, "ventricular septal defect was closed using a patch of autologous pericardium secured with a running 5-0 Prolene on a BV1 needle." It's said that, "the heart has reasons which reason knows not of." It also has a language that's pretty hard to understand as well.

I told Dr. G this was my first time in the OR and I couldn't believe I'd just seen a kid's heart beating inside her chest.

"You've never seen that before?" she asked me.

I reminded her that I'd spent the last 30 years as a sportscaster.

"It's not exactly the kind of thing you see in the Dallas Cowboys locker room," I said.

She was genuinely surprised at my sense of wonder.

The rest of her day consisted of phone calls, emails, consults with other surgeons, afternoon rounds through the CVICU (which move more quickly than morning rounds, as these are just for checking up on each patient one more time), and the never-ending battle with paperwork.

On rounds at 7:30 tomorrow morning, Dr. G will check up on Claudia to see how she's doing. That's assuming she makes it through the night easily. If problems develop, Dr. G could spend the night here with her.

"We eat stress like M&Ms in here," said Dave Bartoo, her surgical tech today.

This is where Dr. Kristine Guleserian repairs the tiny hearts of tiny children.

Come on in.

CHAPTER TWO

Rylynn

"I just want to be Mommy!"

Andrea Riojas went to her OB/GYN on December 23, 2008 for her four-month sonogram. She was pregnant for the first time, and she and her husband Gilly hoped this visit would be the one where they'd find out if they were going to have a boy or a girl. A successful young couple living in central Texas, Gilly is a broad-shouldered, quiet rancher with alert, piercing eyes while Andrea—blonde, cheerful, and ready to be a mom—is an architect specializing in designing healthcare facilities.

"I went in for my twenty-week ultrasound," Andrea recalled, "and we got the feeling right away that something wasn't right. My OB really didn't tell us anything because this was outside of his specialty. He said he'd need to send us to a specialist."

Christmas, with its promise of miracle birth, couldn't have been a more ironic time to get this kind of news and the Riojas family holiday became something less than cheerful. Andrea and Gilly waited two weeks for the specialist appointments the obstetrician recommended. At an appointment with a fetal-maternal specialist, they finally heard the diagnosis. Their baby, a girl, had hypoplastic left heart syndrome. Her left ventricle, which normally sends oxygen-rich blood through the aorta to the rest of the body, was severely underdeveloped. The specialists laid the cards on the table.

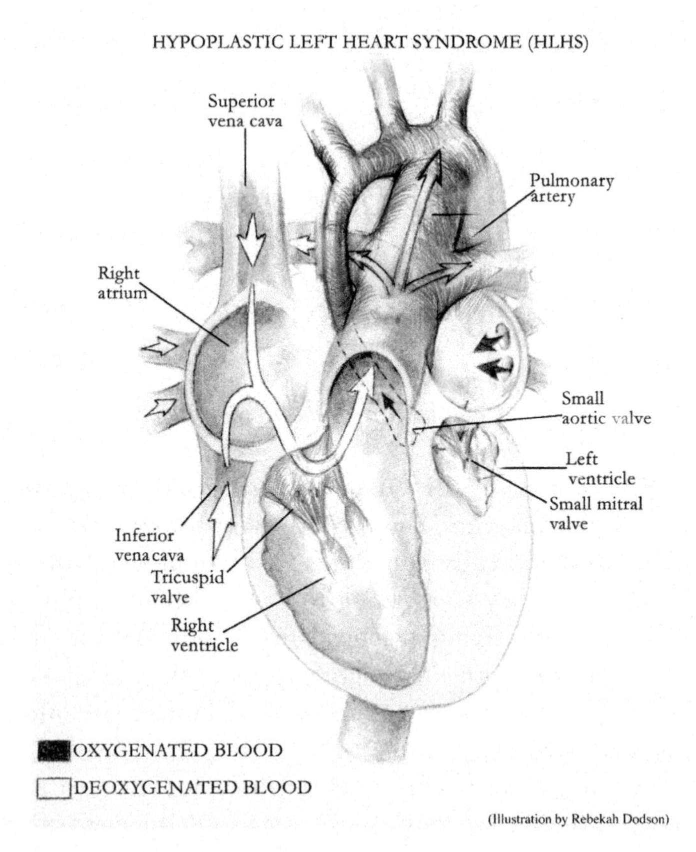

(Illustration by Rebekah Dodson)

"They told us we had three options," Andrea said. "We could terminate the pregnancy; we could proceed with the pregnancy and then either get hospice care after birth or take our baby home where we'd only have a few days with her; or we could proceed with a course of three surgeries which were usually quite successful, but were full of the risks of open-heart surgery— the complications and the risk of fatality. Obviously, we had tremendous emotional ups and downs, and everything in between."

In the end, their choice was really no choice at all. Andrea and Gilly wanted a child and they decided to go ahead with the pregnancy and birth, and the subsequent surgical treatment. The parents-to-be chose the name Rylynn for their unborn daughter, and after numerous meetings with doctors at major hospitals around

Texas, they decided Rylynn would be treated at Children's Medical Center.

More bad news came midway through March, during a meeting with their cardiologist at Children's. An echocardiogram showed that Rylynn's patent foramen ovale, the hole between her left and right atria, was closing. This is a normal development once the child has been born, but for Rylynn, still in utero with a single ventricle anatomy, it was not good. The hole is there to re-route oxygenated blood from the near-useless left ventricle to the right ventricle for pumping around the body. One ventricle has to do the work of two. Moments after she was born, Rylynn would have to undergo a procedure to keep the atrial septum open.

Rylynn Riojas entered the world at 8:37 AM on May 1, 2009. She was delivered by Caesarean section at Parkland Hospital, the county hospital situated next door to Children's. Due to her delicate medical condition, Rylynn did not get a chance to bond immediately with her mother.

"I didn't get to hold her, or touch her, or anything. I remember hearing her scream and it sounded like a duck. And I remember Gilly telling me that she had lots of hair. But then, they whisked her off to Children's, to the cardiac catheterization lab, to treat her atrial septum.

"Not only did I not get to bond with her, but Gilly took off with the doctors and nurses who were wheeling her through the corridors to the cath lab. I finally got to see a picture of her three hours after she was born. It was kind of tough."

But Gilly returned from the cath lab sooner than Andrea expected, and the news was good. The hole between the atria now allowed for a perfect balance between flow and resistance to get Rylynn off to a good start. In the strange surroundings of a hospital, with a child wired to so many machines that they couldn't even hold her, the new parents tried their best to enjoy their first moments of family life.

The treatment of HLHS requires three surgical procedures, each of which is a palliative, not a cure. The first of those procedures, called a Norwood, can carry significant risk. Nationally,

20% of the babies who have the surgery die during their first hospitalization, and one-third die within their first year, within their first year, although the figures for Children's are much better than the national averages. Rylynn's procedure would include placement of a Sano shunt to connect the right ventricle to the pulmonary artery, the blood vessel feeding the lungs. Dr. Joseph Forbess, Chief of Pediatric Cardiothoracic Surgery at Children's, had met the family prenatally and performed this first procedure on May fifth.

"It's really tough to say good bye to your four-day-old baby like that," Andrea said. "It was a very long day. We got hourly updates on the surgery from the OR, and finally we got to see her when it was done. After the surgery, day by day, they'd take out another of her chest wires or drains, and cut out another medicine. Finally, she was extubated and we actually got to hear her cry for the first time!"

A normal CVICU stay after a Norwood is 10 to 14 days. Rylynn was moved to the eighth-floor cardiology ward after only six days. To make it even sweeter, Rylynn's feeding tube was removed. These were the first indications of the toughness this tiny child showed during a battle that would inspire the host of professionals at Children's Medical Center involved in her care. She became what the hospital staff likes to call a "rock star."

On Mother's Day, Andrea held Rylynn in her arms for the first time.

Andrea and Gilly had to remain within quick driving distance of Children's after Rylynn's discharge, keeping her in position to be transported for her second surgery when the time came. The wait wasn't long. By the time she was two months old her oxygen level was fluctuating and doses of Lasix were administered to counteract fluid buildup, all in an effort to buy time. Rylynn and her parents headed back to Children's in September for the second procedure, called a bi-directional Glenn shunt. On September 24, 2009, Dr. Forbess connected Rylynn's superior vena cava to the right branch of her pulmonary artery, so that deoxygenated blood from the upper body, head, chest, and arms traveled directly to the lungs, increasing the amount of blood receiving oxygen. Like the

Norwood, the Glenn is a palliative. There would be more surgery down the line.

Rylynn again displayed amazing recuperative powers, going from the CVICU to the ward only 24 hours after surgery. However, along with the usual post-operative recovery discomfort, this time she had severe headaches.

"She screamed hysterically every 15 to 20 minutes," according to Andrea, "but after a while, she'd gotten through the worst of it and was able to quiet down and rest."

Andrea and Gilly tried resting as well, sleeping on the narrow pullout couch in Rylynn's room. The uncomfortable bed, and more, did not go unnoticed by Andrea, the designer of healthcare facilities. The time spent with her daughter in all those hospitals would have a major impact on Andrea's design work later on.

Everything looked great in June of 2010, when 13-month-old Rylynn had a visit with her cardiologist. Her oxygen saturation was normal, her heart function good. The doctor told the pleased parents they wouldn't need to bring their daughter back for at least six months. But Rylynn developed a viral infection on October first, which led to a severe earache. She spent a couple of days at Dell Children's Hospital in Austin, where doctors tried to get her oxygen level corrected and help her shed the bug she'd picked up. Even a routine virus is a severe threat to a child with a damaged heart. Rylynn visited her Austin cardiologist in late October, and once again the news was not good. Her single ventricle heart wasn't working well enough to keep her growing properly.

"I asked the cardiologist how concerned we should be," Andrea said, "and before I even finished the question, he said, 'Very.'"

Another holiday came to be associated with bad news. This time, it was Thanksgiving. Dr. Matthew Lemler, Rylynn's cardiologist at Children's, recommended that she be brought back to Dallas as soon as possible for transplant evaluation. Rylynn was admitted for a cardiac catheterization and a number of other procedures the first week of December. At the same time, she underwent a rigorous workup for transplant. After the exhaustive evaluation for various criteria—psychological, physical, financial, nutritional, and more—Rylynn was listed for transplant as United Network for Organ Sharing (UNOS) status two, meaning she was on the list, but nowhere near the top. She might wait for years.

Now came the part Andrea and Gilly hoped to avoid. From the moment she was put on the transplant list Rylynn could never be more than two hours away from Dallas. The family home in Lampasas, 180 miles to the southwest, was outside the two-hour area. A duplex was found near Waco, 90 minutes south of Dallas. Gilly would now have to split time between his family and his ranch responsibilities.

"They told us that a transplant was now our only option. They also let us know that a transplant replaces one set of problems with another. But Gilly and I both felt this would give her the best quality of life. We knew she'd be on medication the rest of her life. We knew the new heart would grow with her, but that eventually it would have to be replaced. But we wanted to give her that quality of life."

Just after her second birthday, in May of 2011, Rylynn took a big turn for the worse. Her oxygen saturation levels were dangerously low. Her pediatrician in Waco put Rylynn on oxygen and told Andrea they needed to go straight to Children's. The pediatrician said Rylynn would have to stay on oxygen, and that it was too dangerous for Andrea to drive her in that condition. A transport aircraft was dispatched from Children's to Waco to pick up mother and daughter for yet another chapter in the lengthening hospital saga. Rylynn was admitted directly to the CVICU. Doctors put in a peripherally inserted central catheter (PICC) line to deliver drugs directly to her heart.

"While there were no major changes in her physically," said Andrea, "it became apparent that her tough little heart just couldn't keep up anymore. Gilly and I were really scared, because at this point we were no longer just treading water, we were going under a little bit."

The tough two-year-old weathered this storm, too, and they went back to their temporary home on June fourth. Four days later the truth of Rylynn's condition, and the 24-hour-a-day vigil needed to keep her safe, began to overwhelm Andrea.

"I hate PICC lines," she wrote in the blog she kept during Rylynn's illness. "I have kept it dry, clean, and I check it at least four times per day, but that does no good at all. We have something leaking that we can't figure out. We have to have it redressed for the third time in five days. With each redressing, we risk infection, and it just plain hurts Rylynn.

"I'm not a nurse. I don't want to be a nurse. I want to be Mommy. Only Mommy!"

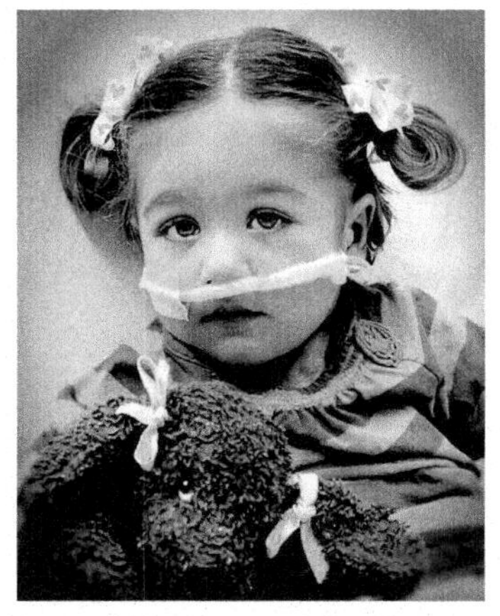

The problems with the PICC line were more than the local home-health nurses could deal with. The line began to leak, and Andrea found herself once again heading to Children's with Rylynn, this time by ambulance.

"It was a little nerve-wracking. Before we even left Waco, the driver locked himself out of the ambulance. Then, while we were speeding up I-35, he was texting a lot of the time. Finally, I asked him if he drove to Children's often and he said he had, and that he'd driven to Dallas at least 300 times in the last four years. Then, he asked me if I knew what exit he should take to get to the hospital."

Rylynn's PICC line had to be replaced. She was released after a three-day stay, and she and Andrea returned to Waco.

Rylynn was back at Children's in June, first to have the PICC line replaced with a Broviac, a different type of central catheter that's a bit more secure in placement, especially in a two-year old. The main purpose of this visit, though, was to confront the reality of her failing liver and kidneys. Her severely compromised heart couldn't support her vital functions much longer. Her failing heart was beginning to affect her other vital organs. She was on maximal medical therapy, which supported her failing ventricular function.

Because of the increased medication, she was now status 1A for transplant, at the top of the list.

Andrea and Gilly noticed the distinct changes in their little girl's health and attitude. Her breathing was labored and she was showing a lot of swelling. Her heart was failing. It was time to meet with Dr. Guleserian.

CHAPTER THREE

Fenway Park and Cardiac Karma – Part 1

"Oh ... and he likes baseball."

It was a chilly October night. Boston's famed Fenway Park was packed with 36,370 baseball fans ready for game two of the 2007 World Series between the Colorado Rockies and the hometown Red Sox. Bright green grass stretched out to the towering left field wall, the famous "Green Monster." On the pitcher's mound Andrew Madden was focused. He adjusted his cap, the famous blue one with the red "B" on it. He held the baseball loosely in his right hand and kicked at the dirt. Some fans wondered if Madden was trying to pitch again too soon. He wasn't recuperating from a sore hamstring, or even a torn rotator cuff. No pitcher had ever come back from the surgery he'd just had and taken to the mound again.

The crowd went silent. Fueled by the adrenaline only his first World Series game could provide, Madden wound up and let loose with a fastball. But there was nobody in the batter's box. His pitch bounced harmlessly in the dirt in front of the catcher who scooped it into his mitt with a practiced ease, trotted out toward the smiling pitcher and handed him the ball. The 36,370 broke into a deafening roar. Madden never imagined hearing such a sound—not in this city, not in this way.

Only three weeks earlier, 13-year-old Andrew Madden lay under anesthesia on the operating table in OR-6 at Children's Medical Center. His chest was cut open through the mid-line of the sternum, his blood routed from his body through a heart-lung bypass machine to feed oxygen to organs and tissues. His diseased heart, enlarged to more than twice its normal size, was being cut out and replaced with the healthy heart of a 24-year-old woman. She died earlier that day, only ten days after giving birth to her first child. Now, even as her family grieved, she was giving birth again. She was nearly twice Andrew's age, but because she was slender and had the same blood type, her heart was the perfect size for him.

Andrew Madden began his comeback in Boston—the completion of a heart journey that took him from Children's Medical Center to Fenway Park. Andrew's transplant surgeon, friend, and fellow Red Sox fanatic was Dr. Guleserian. Dr. G had taken the journey in reverse, going from Boston to Dallas, where her path intersected with Andrew's.

* * *

August, 2007, and Dr. G hurried through the Children's Medical Center hallway at her typical, rapid pace when a cardiologist stopped her and said she might want to check with the echo lab to get information on a case just admitted from west Texas. She detoured to the lab and first "met" Andrew Madden. One glance at his echo showed her what most people would call an enlarged heart. She knew this was idiopathic dilated cardiomyopathy.

The first word of the diagnosis, "idiopathic," means we don't know why it happens. It's from the Greek, "idios" meaning "unknown or obscure," and "pathos," meaning "suffering." It's a process by which the heart muscle, over time, dilates—it gets thinner while the ventricular cavity size gets larger. In some of these cases the heart function gets better, in some it stays the same for years, and some people, like Andrew, get worse. It's roughly a third, a third, and a third.

The danger with cardiomyopathy is that heart function becomes less efficient as the heart dilates. The pumping action can become so weak that patients like Andrew are in danger of total heart failure. From birth, it was obvious that Andrew wasn't normal. His heart function was mildly inefficient, but with medication he could be stabilized and live a normal, healthy life, which he did for thirteen years.

When you grow up in Odessa, Texas much of life is as it used to be decades ago. Kids play baseball all day, and they make sure to add "Sir" or "Ma'am" to the end of a sentence when speaking to a grownup. Andrew was a normal Odessa kid. Little League baseball, basketball, school. It was on the local par-three golf course where Andrew's life all but sliced into the woods for good.

"It was mid-August," his mother Lauri Wemmer told MLB.COM, "and he was trying out a new set of golf clubs. I was with him. All of a sudden he fell to his knees and began gasping for air. He was showing all the signs of heart failure. He had reached the point where his heart was barely pumping."

Andrew was rushed to Dallas by air ambulance and admitted to Children's. He and his mother had 13 years to understand his life and his heart. Dr. G had less than a day to take it all in, analyze the salient points, and make critical decisions. Because she was the Surgical Director of Cardiac Transplantation at Children's, Andrew's case was referred to her by his primary cardiologist. Her decision-making process began in the echo lab, where the extent of the problem was clear. Dr. G and the cardiologists were all on the same page about the course Andrew needed to take.

We began to treat him medically with the understanding that if his clinical condition worsened significantly while he was waiting for a new heart, and his other organs began to suffer, we might have to implant a ventricular assist device (VAD), *a pump to essentially take over for his failing while he awaited a new one—what we call a "bridge to transplantation."*

Andrew was a vigorous, athletic teenager. He would not have enjoyed life restricted by the bulk and inconvenience of a VAD. Yet whenever it happened, transplantation would bring its own problems and restrictions. Having a diseased heart replaced with a healthy one may seem like a cure, but with transplantation you're really trading one disease for another. All transplant patients require immunosuppression medication for the rest of their lives, to make certain their immune systems don't perceive the transplanted part as a foreign organ and try to reject it. They also face psychological scars just as real, and often more prominent, than the physical ones. Whether it's the length of time the patient is under anesthesia, or simply the emotional turmoil the patient and family experience throughout the ordeal, not everybody bounces back from a transplant to lead a completely normal life. Add to that the problems a young teen faces dealing with adolescence and raging hormones, working out the boundaries of his soon-to-be-adult life, and the picture becomes even more complex.

We compared Andrew's echocardiograms done over the years and we saw clear progressive dilation and deterioration of heart function. Andrew's family knew he might need a transplant at some point. Now, that time had come. Andrew showed no signs of end organ dysfunction. His kidneys, liver, and intestines were working normally at this point. He was a rock star transplant candidate. He had a very supportive family engaged and invested in his care. He was articulate and smart, and he understood the disease process and what it would take to come through it as a recipient. He was motivated to do what we required of him. He had a great attitude. Following our transplant evaluation, he was deemed a suitable candidate, and was immediately added onto the transplant list.

Andrew and his family were given a pager. The moment a donor heart was located, the pager would buzz. No matter where he was or what he was doing, at that moment everything else in his life would have to stop, and he would be prepared for surgery to replace his heart with a heart from someone else.

* * *

The surgeon's first meeting with the patient is always important, especially in the pediatric setting. A good doctor tries to establish trust and friendship immediately. When the surgery involved is something as serious as a heart transplant, doctors have to be able to count on the patient becoming another member of the surgical team. Dr. G talked with Andrew's cardiologist at Children's,

Dr. Lynn Mahony, wanting to know more than just what could be seen on the echo or in his chart. Many doctors refer to patients in the abstract, as "the appendectomy in 240." But there are parts of American's convoluted medical system that work well when run by people who truly care. Dr. G will most often refer to a patient by name, or as "this little cutie" or "this little guy." For the moment Dr. G wanted to know about Andrew's personality, his likes and dislikes, his hobbies: not just *what* he was—*who* he was.

In a nutshell, what Dr. Mahony told me was he's a skinny, pale kid who hasn't gained a single pound over the last year. That's very unusual for an adolescent, and so you knew something was really wrong with him. And then as she walked away, she turned back and said, "Oh, and he likes baseball."

Armed with that small amount of personal information, the images she reviewed on the monitor in the echo lab, and the data from Andrew's medical chart, Dr. G went to the eighth-floor cardiology ward for the first face-to-face encounter. In the hallway outside his room, she saw a pale, skinny kid standing with an IV pole. She knew immediately it was Andrew, and at first glance he wasn't any different from a hundred other patients. Then they began to talk, and the first meeting of the heart surgeon and the young patient became something out of a storybook.

CHAPTER FOUR

Family and Early Education

"If I studied Greek, I'd understand everything.
I'd have the foundation for it all."

There's a photo that's famous in the Guleserian family, taken when Dr. G was three-year old Krissie. It's one of those rare family photos that offers a glimpse into the future as it captures the past—as if you stumbled across a photo of a young Bob Dylan strumming his first guitar.

This was back in the day when boys got the toy doctor kit and girls got the toy nurse kit. That's why I have the nurse hat on. Also, I happen to be wearing my mother's lingerie, which I used to do all the time, and which drove her crazy. That's my dad lying on the floor, being the "patient." I was "examining" him, and my brother Michael, in his Boston Bruins pajamas, was watching. He probably didn't understand why I was listening to my father's heart on the right side of his chest instead of the left. I was three years old and I didn't have time to explain to my one-year old brother that I was checking for dextrocardia, a rare congenital condition where the heart points to the right side of the body instead of the left! I was obviously meant to become a congenital heart surgeon.

Kris was no stranger to congenital heart problems, even from her early childhood in Cambridge. She had no idea that one day she'd be treating sick kids, but she learned early on that kids get sick.

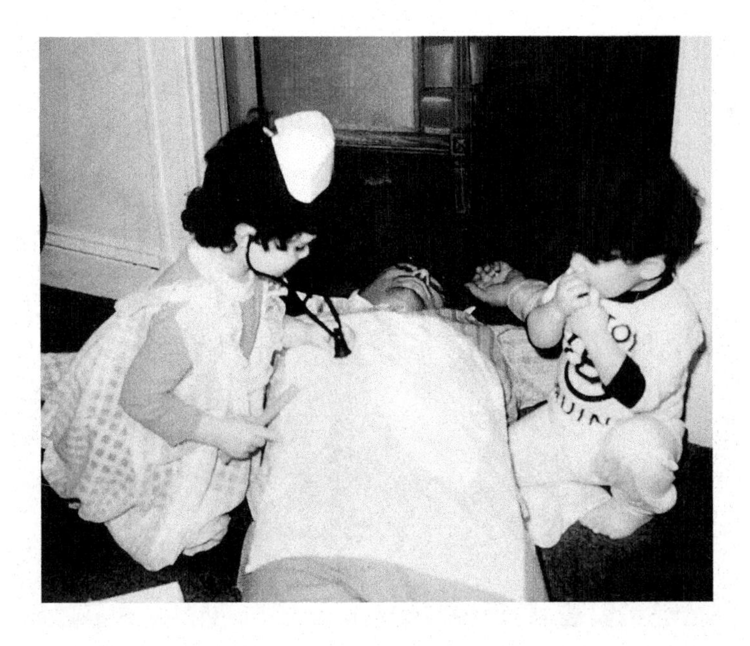

My parents, Edward and Nancy, were married June 3, 1967 and I was born April 20, 1968. My brother Michael was born February 21, 1970. He had a heart murmur at birth that was detected by our pediatrician, Dr. T. Berry Brazelton, and was subsequently diagnosed with tetralogy of Fallot by Dr. Donald Fyler, a well-known pediatric cardiologist. My brother had all the classic signs and symptoms of tetralogy of Fallot. He'd say, "Mom, I'm tired," and then just face-plant right into his dinner. I remember his lips turning blue, and he'd squat all the time, classic symptoms—TOF kids squat because they're trying to force more blood to the heart to overcome the pulmonary stenosis, the obstruction of blood flow to the lungs. When he was two years old, he had his first heart surgery, a classic Blalock-Taussig shunt. That was the classic treatment in the early 1970s. He had his second surgery, full repair of his TOF, in 1976. Then in 2015, 43 years after his first surgery, he underwent pulmonary valve implantation.

Her brother's frequent trips to the doctor gave Kris even more exposure to medicine. And visits to their pediatrician were special moments.

Edward, Nancy, Michael, and Kris Guleserian.

I loved—and to this day still love—Dr. Brazelton. He's a world-renowned pediatrician with the most comforting bedside manner. We were so lucky to have him in our lives. He was born and raised in Waco, Texas, and attended Princeton. He's now in his nineties, and he's a professor emeritus at Harvard. He wrote the book "What Every Baby Knows," a huge bestseller. Because Michael had to have frequent visits, I would go with him. When one of us needed to go to the doctor, everybody went. I was fascinated with Dr. Brazelton. His office was on Hawthorne Street in Cambridge, in Harvard Square. It was walking distance from the Sheraton Commander Hotel, where we lived until I was eight years old and which my family still owns and runs. Dr. Brazelton's office was in the basement of his home. He would always ask who wanted to go first. I knew my eyesight wasn't perfect, so I always said my brother should be first. Then, I'd sit in the exam room and memorize the eye chart because I didn't want to have glasses. I was playing field hockey and lacrosse in high school, and my distance vision wasn't great, so I finally got contacts. After that, I was a much better scorer! I finally told Dr. Brazelton about the eye chart thing in 2016 when we met for brunch, and he thought it was hysterical.

As if the familial heart episodes weren't distressing enough, another neighborhood boy had heart problems as well.

There was another little boy in our elementary school, Belmont Day School in Belmont, Massachusetts, who had a congenital heart defect. His name was Tommy. Tommy had a diagnosis of double outlet right ventricle. Both of the great arteries, his aorta and pulmonary artery, arose from the right ventricle, so deoxygenated blood was being pumped not only to his lungs, where it should go, but to the rest of his body as well. Tommy developed pulmonary hypertension. He would get really blue, he'd struggle to breathe, and he was cachectic, meaning he was wasting away. He had two older brothers who always helped him onto the school bus every day. I remember, at the age of ten, wondered why nothing could be done for Tommy. He was our schoolmate and close friend. But you have to remember this was the 1970s, well before transplantation was a reality for children. It wasn't until 1984 and the "Baby Fae" case that pediatric heart transplant became a reality.

Years later, Tommy's parents told me that for his ninth birthday all he wanted was to eat a lobster, play baseball in the backyard, and hit a home run. So, at his ninth birthday party he ate a lobster. He went out in his backyard dressed in his Red Sox uniform to play baseball, Tommy loved the Red Sox as we all do, and sure enough, he hit a home run. He went back inside and told his mom and dad he was tired, went in to take a nap, and never woke up again.

Up to that point, I thought only old people died. Now I'd look at my little brother and think, "Gosh, is he going to die, too?" He already had his Blalock-Taussig shunt as an infant, and had undergone his tetralogy of Fallot repair when he was six. He seemed perfectly OK, but those thoughts would go through my head. My brother and Tommy were in Boston Children's Hospital at the same time, we lived just a few streets away from each other, went to the same school. And both my mother and Tommy's mother were named Nancy. It was just kind of unsettling. As a kid, you never know: "Will my brother be here tomorrow?"

Medicine began to call to Kris at an early age, encouraging an abiding love of books and study. She spent her recess time in the library at Belmont Day School.

There was a book I loved to read at the library when I was very young. It had some kind of animation with it—probably microfiche type video—in the back of the book. It was a series of x-ray images of a person eating a banana. The banana was coated with contrast material, so you could see the banana being chewed up and making its way down the esophagus into the stomach. I'd watch it over and over and I thought it was the coolest thing I'd ever seen. The other example I watched was someone swallowing a contrast-coated marshmallow. I was fascinated. I think that may have further tweaked my interest in the human body and medicine.

Her mother taught her how to get things done, and imbued in her daughter the kindess and caring that led to development of sympathetic bedside manner. A good portion of the consistency and perfectionist tendencies that have served Dr. G so well came to Kris from her father.

My dad was an engineer. And he loved to grow things. Early every spring he'd map out his garden on graph paper, row by row. How close should the tomato plants be to each other so they'd all grow properly? What type of tomato should go where? He was very patient and precise. The family joke was that with my dad, everything was very careful—don't rush. And with my mom, everything was urgent, everything had to be done immediately. For example, if I forgot socks at home after a visit, she'd send them back to me overnight. Once my mom baked some of her famous walnut chocolate-chip cookies and gave them to my dad to send to me, thinking he'd send them overnight. He just sent them by normal mail. By the time they arrived they were still edible, but barely. After that, I told him to send the green tomatoes from the end of the season through the mail, so they'd be ripe by the time they got to me. And he did. He would send me a box of tomatoes, each one was wrapped in its own little wrapper, even each little cherry tomato. He'd call to ask if they got there OK, if there was any damage, and how their color was.

Another trait Kris got from her father was the desire to never miss out on the action. Ambulance chasing became a family art form.

There was a TV show that was really big back in those days called, 'Emergency.' It was about a paramedic team in the Los Angeles Fire Department. They'd get a call—it could be a cat stuck in a tree, and then someone in a bad car accident, then someone who just had a heart attack. I loved that show. So, one day my dad got us a police scanner. We were really excited. Well, not my mom, but my brother and I were. Now we could actually monitor the local police calls live. When we'd hear where a call was he'd say, "OK kids, let's go," and we'd jump in the car and track down the accident. I always loved the action, the "What's going on?" aspect. It drove my mother crazy, but the three of us loved it. And to this day, if there's a wreck on the highway, I try to drive carefully, but I always look back to check it out and see what's going on.

In high school, Kris was introduced to a subject that would fascinate her the rest of her life.

I went to a small, private school called The Winsor School, only 48 students in my graduating class, all girls. One of our mandatory classes was Latin, but everything we translated and read in that class was about war—everything. One day Mrs. Dorothy Souvaine, the Greek teacher, told me about the great storytelling nature inherent to Greek literature and that I should give it a try. Then she wrote out the entire Greek alphabet and a few simple Greek words. The first word she wrote down was "Bios," meaning life. And then she wrote "Logos," meaning study of. Bioslogos. Biology—the study of life. I was fascinated. If I studied and became proficient in Greek, I could dissect out every word and understand its true meaning. I'd have the fundamentals to understand it all.

I wrote my expository writing paper in high school on the subject of autopsies. My dad knew Dr. David Dow, the medical examiner in Cambridge, where we lived. Dr. Dow introduced me to the work of the famous forensic pathologists who investigated the celebrity deaths. I was fascinated by it all. I went to the Boston Public

Library and checked out all the books I could find about autopsies. Some of them were incredibly graphic because they dealt with Mafia killings, and had photos of people who were dismembered and put in suitcases and things. The school actually banned one of the books I had because it was so disturbing. But it was fascinating to me. I read every page of it.

Just as there aren't enough hours in the day for Dr. G to finish her to-do list as a surgeon, as a student there was never enough time for all the activities Kris wanted to take part in.

In school, I was always on the go. I was studying French, Latin, and Greek, and playing sports. I was doing so much I drove my parents crazy. I had to go school 45 minutes or an hour early. I played field hockey, lacrosse, and squash. I wanted to play soccer, too, but the Winsor School didn't have soccer at the time. I had to go back to Belmont and play in the town soccer league. I had all of these activities going on. I wanted to play violin because my dad played violin, and I had to do everything my dad did. I was terrible on the violin. But my poor mother, she'd get us off to school and go back to her day. She'd be driving by the bus stop and see that I'd left my violin, so she'd get it. It must have worn her down, because I came home one day and she said, "That's it—no more violin—you're taking piano lessons!"

Dr. G remains close to the Winsor School, and returned as an honored guest for an emotional ceremony.

I went back to the Winsor School in 2011 to give the annual Virginia Wing Lecture. Miss Wing was the headmistress of the Winsor School when I was there. She was amazing and to this day has always been a role model for me. When I was a student at the Winsor School Dr. Tenley Albright, a gold medal Olympic figure skater who became a general surgeon, spoke to the student body in the very same assembly room I was now going to speak in. Dr. Albright's speech made a huge impression on me. I thought, "Wow, a woman can be a surgeon!" And now I was a woman and a surgeon and speaking to the student body. I can go to a surgical conference and speak in front of 1,500 surgeons and they'll all listen to what I have to say and then they'll all go off to the next talk.

But if I'm talking to a room full of students, I feel like everybody's listening, they almost all have questions, they're all interested and the impact I can make there is huge.

The Winsor School administrators asked me if there were any special guests I'd like to have in the audience for my talk. In addition to my family I immediately thought of Dr. Brazelton and his wife, Christina, who was a Winsor alumna. So, they were sent an invitation. Then I got a letter from Dr. Brazelton—he always sends handwritten notes—and he said he was sorry, but he couldn't attend because he had to go to Washington, D.C. to consult with President Obama about the Affordable Care Act. I took a picture of his note and showed it to the girls at school during my talk. I told them, "The White House? What a lame excuse! But clearly, Dr. Brazelton came to his senses, because he's here today with his wife, Christina." Later, at a reception, he took out an index card with the data from the last physical I had in his Hawthorne Street office, and he read out my height, weight, and vital signs from when I was 17 years old! In front of everyone! I couldn't believe he still had it.

Dr. Guleserian and Dr. T. Berry Brazelton

CHAPTER FIVE

Intervention

"We had to do something."

Dr. Guleserian knew of Rylynn's case almost from the start. Her surgical partner, Dr. Joe Forbess, performed Rylynn's first two surgeries, and the surgeons often briefed each other on cases. In her capacity as surgical director of transplantation, Dr. G was part of the team that evaluated Rylynn and approved her listing for transplant the previous December. Rylynn and her failing heart worked their way on to Dr. G's caseload for good when the two-year-old was admitted to Children's on July 18, 2011.

When I was first called to the CVICU it was obvious that Rylynn was in severe heart and lung failure. She was on the verge of intubation. In December, she was in heart failure but, as is often the case, the cardiac transplant team could manage her as an outpatient on oral heart failure therapy. By May she needed IV milrinone (to increase the heart's pumping function and decrease vascular resistance) *and that's when her UNOS status was bumped up to 1A. Her heart was failing but at least her other organs—her kidneys, liver, and intestines—were still OK. Now, in July, things were much worse—she looked terrible. The IV milrinone was already maxed out. I didn't think she would survive.*

It wasn't just her heart. Her other organs were failing because of low cardiac output, so the next logical step was mechanical circulatory support. But Rylynn was already a high-risk transplant candidate. Not only was she a single-ventricle patient, she was what we call 'highly sensitized.' She had markedly elevated panel-reactive-antibodies (PRA—the higher the PRA number, the more difficult it would be to find a matching heart) *from her prior surgeries and from exposure to blood products. We knew that if we implanted a ventricular assist device, in her case one called a Berlin Heart, she would be exposed to more blood products, which theoretically could increase her already high antibody level, making it even more difficult to find a suitable donor heart. Unfortunately, you never know when a donor heart will be available. There is no crystal ball. Knowing that only one-third of single-ventricle patients who are on VAD support even survive to transplant, the odds were against her. But we had a child whose heart was failing right in front of our eyes. We had to do something.*

* * *

Beginning in the early 20th century, different artificial hearts and ventricular-assist devices were developed by any number of people not always trained in medicine. In the 1930s, Alexis Carrel and Charles Lindbergh created one of the earliest perfusion devices, designed to supply blood to a body organ to keep it alive. Each man was already world famous. French physician Carrel won the Nobel Prize in medicine in 1912 for his vascular suturing techniques. Lindbergh was the first man to fly solo across the Atlantic, in 1927. The perfusion device they invented was never used with humans, but it was their theory that led to the development of the heart-lung bypass machine in use today. In the 1950s Paul Winchell, a popular children's television ventriloquist, designed a rudimentary artificial heart, among many other inventions. Winchell met Dr. Henry Heimlich, the man credited with the maneuver to prevent people from choking on food, and Heimlich encouraged Winchell to work to improve his artificial heart design. Winchell patented the heart in the early 1960s. It was never used in human patients.

The first patient to receive an artificial heart was Barney Clark, a dentist, in 1982. He lived for over three months tethered to a machine weighing 400 pounds, powering the device in his chest. Dr. Michael DeBakey and Dr. Denton Cooley, two legendary heart surgeons from Houston, contributed significantly to the development of artificial valves, and the total artificial heart. The technology dreamed of in those earlier days would play a major role in Rylynn's treatment. But before they could take advantage of technology, the team treating Rylynn had to deal with bureaucracy.

The Berlin Heart is a German invention, as its name would suggest. It's a ventricular-assist device designed to augment or totally replace ventricular function in patients with end-stage heart failure. The Berlin Heart wasn't even approved by the Food & Drug Administration for pediatric use in the US during the period when Rylynn's condition was worsening, except on a case-by-case "compassionate use" basis.

While we were taking care of Rylynn, trying to do the right thing for her, I couldn't reach anybody from the FDA or the insurance companies to get the special approval required to implant a Berlin Heart in a pediatric patient. I was at the mercy of the system, watching Rylynn get sicker because it wasn't normal business hours. It always seemed like every holiday weekend a child like Rylynn would be admitted to the CVICU in the middle of the night in de-compensated heart failure, maxed out on medical therapy, and in urgent need of mechanical support. But the government and the insurance companies only work Monday through Friday, nine to five—no holidays.

Rylynn was born with hypoplastic left heart syndrome. Her left ventricle never worked. And now her right ventricle, her only functioning ventricle, was failing. Rylynn initially did very well, but she developed severe right ventricular dysfunction and severe tricuspid regurgitation. Her right ventricle, her only pump, was failing, and the valve between her right atrium and right ventricle was leaking badly. She would never be a candidate for the Fontan procedure, the third in the series of surgeries for kids with HLHS. The only surgical option would be a heart transplant.

Not everybody who needs a heart is automatically an eligible candidate for transplantation. There's a rigorous order of medical, logistical, and financial considerations for people seeking a place on the list. U.S. Department of Health and Human Services statistics show that an average of 79 people get organ transplants every day in the United States, while 22 people who are waiting for transplants die. Recent statistics show that on a given day, some 400 children are on the waiting list for new hearts, and around 50 die each year while on the list and waiting. Supply and demand is the first barrier.

Andrea and Rylynn in the Children's Medical Center CVICU.

Rylynn was officially on the transplant list, but nobody knew when a donor heart would become available. Berlin Heart implantation meant another round of open-heart surgery, more time on the pump, more blood thinners, and a new list of potential complications. Rylynn and her family would have to adjust to living with external tubing and a pump moving blood into and out of her body, possible infection, the need for more blood products adding to her PRA problem, and the added risk of potentially fatal bleeding and clotting. Rylynn was now committed to living in the hospital until a donor heart became available. Rylynn's family was waiting for somebody else to die.

On July 21, 2011, Rylynn was again kissed by her parents and taken to the OR, this time for the implantation of a Berlin

Heart-EXCOR, standing for "extra-corporeal," meaning the mechanical pump is outside the chest. Dr. G wrote in her operative report that Rylynn's "liver was palpable (able to be felt) down to her right iliac crest and well across the midline. Her transaminases (an enzyme to catalyze amino acid reaction—an important indicator of liver damage) and INR (a blood-clotting indicator) were markedly elevated, she was severely hypoalbuminemic (low levels of protein in the blood), her creatinine was elevated (indicative of kidney failure) and she was oliguric (not producing sufficient urine), which is indicative of end stage organ dysfunction." In other words, Rylynn's heart had become so weak and inefficient that it was now killing off her own liver and kidneys.

Dr. G ran a scalpel across the already prominent sternotomy scar on Rylynn's chest from her previous surgeries. After sawing open and separating her sternum, Dr. G got her first real look at Rylynn's heart, which she later described as "massively dilated." She spent some time freeing up the adhesions surrounding and obscuring the aorta, vena cavae, and ventricle. As Dr. G freed up the scar tissue, Rylynn's heart rhythm dramatically changed. She went into ventricular fibrillation, a dangerously erratic heartbeat. Her blood wasn't going anywhere.

Dr. G immediately began CPR with open cardiac massage, and then, using defibrillator paddles, shocked the heart back into normal rhythm as if she'd done it a thousand times, which she probably had. It's not nearly as dramatic in the OR as it is on TV. Except that this is a real person and there are no re-takes. Rylynn was given heparin to prevent blood clotting before being placed on the heart-lung bypass machine. Connecting Rylynn to the Berlin Heart meant suturing a cannula in the right ventricle, then sewing another cannula onto the aorta, and tunneling both through the chest wall and into the Berlin Heart pump, all in an effort to supplement the work of her failing right ventricle. The VAD was connected and the Berlin Heart was now the driving force behind Rylynn's circulation. Rylynn was weaned from the heart-lung bypass machine successfully. The transesophageal echo confirmed that everything was in position and the Berlin Heart pump was working properly.

The swelling in Rylynn's liver was already better or, in the words of the operative report, "... it was quite remarkable how her hepatomegaly (liver enlargement) had nearly completely resolved."

Rylynn came out of the OR attached to a blue, file-cabinet-size device. That cabinet was the driving unit of the Berlin Heart pump, controlled by a laptop computer that sat atop it. A small pump, resembling a paperweight with arms, beat outside of Rylynn's chest. Tubes filled with blood ran to and from the pump, to and from her chest. This technology would have to keep her alive until a suitable donor heart was found.

So basically, blood from her right ventricle passes through the inflow cannula, into a pneumatically driven pump, and is redirected back to her aorta via the outflow cannula. The perfectly functioning Berlin Heart pump has essentially replaced her diseased, failing, native heart pump.

Adjusting to life attached to a large machine required both physical and occupational therapy. Rylynn's medications were adjusted—and readjusted—as needed. Only four days out of surgery, the two-year-old could sit up on the edge of her bed, which may not seem like much, but with a series of tubes and gadgets pulling on your chest, your center of gravity becomes displaced, and you have to learn all over again how sitting up actually works.

Andrea and Gilly continued their vigil. Rylynn was able to leave the ICU one week after this latest surgery to visit the hospital lobby for a "Christmas in July" event the Child Life staff organized for patients. When Rylynn's transplant coordinator, Laurie Hinman, heard the tough little girl was eating again she brought Rylynn some Sprinkles cupcakes, the high-end variety. Rylynn ate half a cupcake, her biggest meal since the implantation of her VAD.

It was difficult for Andrea to watch Rylynn go through physical therapy. Her little girl, who should have been running, playing, and carefree, would struggle to stand up, or bend over to pick a ball up off the floor. It was a major effort.

"We were so proud of the way she worked. I know it was hard for her, but she tried her best every time. She can stand up now if she's holding on to something, or holding somebody's hands,"

Andrea wrote in her blog. "The weekends are the best time. There's only one therapy session a day, and a whole lot less people popping in all the time."

Lack of sleep was an issue, and Rylynn was given sedation medication. There are numerous reasons for sleep deprivation after major surgery. The bottom line is that lack of sleep slows healing. Sleep deprivation was one thing to be avoided at all costs.

Rylynn and Andrea were interviewed by the Children's Medical Center public relations department for an ongoing reality TV special called "Children's Med: Dallas." Rylynn's celebrity was beginning to build. That's not surprising, since everybody who walked into her room and saw those huge, gorgeous eyes fell in love with her at first glance. In addition to becoming a celebrity, she was also something of a medical first.

Literally as we were implanting the Berlin Heart in Rylynn, the FDA began the formal process of approving its use in pediatric cases.

CASE NOTES
PATIENT: JENNIFER N.
DOB: 6-11-03

Jennifer had her first heart attack at the age of two. It's understandable. The upper limit for "normal" blood cholesterol levels is around 200 mg/dl (milligrams per deciliter). Jennifer's cholesterol level was 1,020. She had an inherited disorder called homozygous familial hypercholesterolemia. Her liver couldn't metabolize cholesterol. It is, literally, a one-in-a-million diagnosis. Both her parents carry the gene for the condition, and her maternal grandmother died of a heart attack at age 31. Her older brother Frankie was being treated for a milder form of the disorder.

At first her parents thought the scabs on her tiny ankles were just a skin condition. But her Miami pediatrician recognized it as a telltale sign of the deadly disease she carried. The family moved to Texas to take advantage of new treatments being offered, including advancements in plasmapheresis, a filtering of blood plasma to remove cholesterol. Jennifer had her first three treatments at Cook Children's Hospital in Fort Worth, and everything looked good. She had her heart attack during the fourth procedure. She was sent the 35 miles to Children's Medical Center where, after they finished a lengthy workup, doctors told her family that Jennifer needed a rarely performed double transplant. She'd get a new heart and a new liver in the same surgery.

Drs. Michael Brown and Joseph Goldstein did groundbreaking research in cholesterol disorders at UT Southwestern Medical Center in the 1970s. They broke down the genetics of hypercholesterolemia and found the mutation that created it. Their work won the Nobel Prize for Medicine in 1985, and Jennifer was a beneficiary of their efforts. She was admitted to Children's in July, 2006 and listed for transplant August 11th. And that's when the fates began to intervene.

Another name is added to national organ transplant waiting lists every 21 minutes. Waiting for one organ is agonizing enough. Waiting for two is exponentially worse. Especially since the organs have to come from the same donor, at the same time, so both transplants can be accomplished in one surgery. Organs might not become available for weeks, months, or years, if ever. Jennifer's parents were given a pager and told that when it went off, that would be the signal that suitable donor organs had been found. In storytelling that's called the "ticking clock," the added twist of an element of running time. When will the bomb explode? When will the cavalry arrive? How long until the questions are answered? Two days of waiting was more than enough for Jennifer's father Rich. He stood in her hospital room staring at the pager. He squeezed it and angrily said, "Why won't you go off?"

And the pager beeped.

That would be enough for most screenwriters. But now the drama grows.

When you list a patient for a double organ transplant like that, the recipient waiting for two organs has priority over somebody waiting for only one. Two days after listing, I got the page from the OPO (organ procurement organization). *I was on the phone with them and Susan Daneman, our nurse/transplant coordinator, was with me. I told them the heart was perfect and we'd take it. Susan left to inform the family. Just as an afterthought I asked, "We're getting the liver, too, right?" They told me they'd already placed the liver in Houston. I said to Susan, "I don't think so. Get me your medical director." And I told him, "You're going to have make a very difficult phone call to the Houston team and tell them that we get the heart and the liver." And that's what happened.*

The timing was more than good. Jennifer's left anterior descending coronary artery was completely blocked. In the adult world, that would result in the "Widow Maker" heart attack. But tough little Jennifer hung on.

The transplant took place August 14th. As the donor organs made their way to Children's, Dr. G opened Jennifer's chest and saw how things looked. Everybody knew Jennifer was sick, but even Dr. G was surprised at how sick she turned out to be. In her post-op report, Dr. G wrote, "... the patient's ascending aorta was extensively diseased with fatty plaque deposits ... the myocardium was pale." In other words, just in time.

When her new heart was in place, and the clamp was removed from her aorta, the heart began beating in perfect rhythm. Her sternum was closed and wired shut. But she wasn't taken to the CVICU. Instead, another surgical team came in and gave Jennifer her new liver. Dr. G stayed in the OR through the second surgery.

Jennifer made a little bit of history as the youngest child in the world to receive a combined heart-liver transplant. Her brother Frankie, who Dr. G remembers as always being around, and always asking questions about everything, was so impressed by the events in his sister's life that he went to medical school.

CHAPTER SIX

Higher Education

"If you can't operate in heels, you can't operate."

Dr. G's office walls are covered with diplomas, awards and certificates. The display of credentials is important for patient families to see, so they can understand how much training goes into the making of a surgeon. I dropped by her office one day and I saw that instead of covering the walls, her diplomas covered the floor. And she was sitting in the middle of all her framed certificates.

"What are you doing?" I asked.

"I'm going to have all these reframed, so they match," she said. She pointed at one diploma. "See, this one needs a larger frame."

"No," I told her, "out of all of these, that's the last one that needs to be changed. Everybody will notice that one just the way it is."

"Why?"

"Because it says 'Harvard.'"

UNDERGRADUATE STUDY

At Harvard, my concentration was Classics; Greek to be specific. It isn't called a major at Harvard, it's called a concentration. When I told my father that I was going to make Classics my concentration he said, "What the hell are you gonna do with a degree in Greek? Go back and teach at the Winsor School? Because that might be the only job there is." I went back to Boston for my 30th Winsor School reunion not long ago and the irony is that they don't even offer Greek anymore. They teach Chinese now.

Since there was no pre-med concentration at Harvard I used all of my electives to fulfill requirements for medical school—biology, organic chemistry, physics, all of that. But I also took art classes, history of art. I love all kinds of art, particularly contemporary art. I was always fascinated by it.

Her love of classical language expanded at Harvard. She was exposed to just the sort of world-class professors you'd expect to learn from when you wear crimson. But Kris could even be tough on world-class Harvard professors.

I took a Greek writing class called "The Concept of the Hero in Hellenic Civilization" taught by Professor Greg Nagy—great guy, great teacher. He made everything seem exciting. I wrote a paper for the course, and I only got a B. Now, of course the professor doesn't read every paper, his teaching assistants do. But I couldn't believe it. It was supposed to be an easy class. Football players were in this class. It was even nicknamed "Heroes for Zeros." I was a Classics major. I knew my stuff! So, I asked Professor Nagy to read my paper for himself, and if he thought it deserved a B to leave it a B. He read it and said, "You were right, this deserves an A." I don't mind it if I actually don't know something and I'm critiqued for not knowing. But when I do know it, and you tell me I'm wrong—damn it, man, you're going to hear from me!

You might think that studying classical Greek isn't the best way to prep for a surgical career, but discipline in one area can lead to discipline in another.

I was handed a reading list as a freshman and it listed every work by Homer, Sophocles, Aristotle, Aristophanes, Pindar, you name it. At the end of four years, I had a two-day written and oral exam for my honors degree. On day one I had to translate whatever passages they gave me that were in the original Greek, give the historical significance and the context of the work in which it appeared, and write an essay about it. The second day was a full day of oral exams on different passages from the same reading list. It was very much a precursor to my work in surgery, where there are continuing written and oral exams throughout your career.

The obscure nature of her course of study led her down unusual, and typically atypical, Kris-like paths.

Dr. David Mitten was my faculty thesis advisor. He was passionate about Greek art and archeology —it was contagious. One day we were talking about one of his archeological digs in Greece and that's when I came up with the idea to write my honors thesis on Athenian children's burial customs in the fifth and fourth centuries B.C.E.—Before Common Era. Burial customs in ancient Greece were a reflection of the political and financial conditions of the times. If it was an elaborate burial with all kinds of gold trinkets and things, that meant times were good, the economy was good. If it was a cremation, the economy was bad.

I was fascinated by Greek history and philosophy. The ancient Greeks had a great definition of happiness. Croesus, in his Histories, always said that happiness was "seeing the children of your children." Not wealth, or power, but being able to see the children of your children. The Greeks also believed that you never could experience true happiness until you had suffered, so-called "pathos." Pathos, logos, ethos: emotion, logic, and ethics. It was that kind of philosophy that drew me to Classics, to Greek.

One final Harvard story demonstrates that it's not always easy being a Guleserian.

My first semester at Harvard, final exams weren't given until after Christmas, which made it kind of tough to enjoy the vacation. My mother always used to open our house during the holidays to what I called the "stragglers"—all my classmates who didn't have a place to go or who were waiting for their flights back home—she'd feed you no matter what. She'd pretty much have you adopted by the end of dinner. I was home for Christmas after my first semester and I was pretty certain I only got a B in one of the ridiculously difficult math classes I took. When I got home, there was a letter for me from the Harvard Admissions Office and basically it said, "In reviewing your application it appears that your admission to Harvard was an error. While we will allow you to take your final exams and finish the first semester, you will have to complete the rest of your college studies elsewhere."

I was going crazy, thinking, "Jeez, you get a B in one class and they kick you out?" I didn't tell anybody about this. I was sitting at dinner with all my freshman classmates, the stragglers, and my parents were asking everybody, "How's school? How is the first semester going?" And everybody was just as happy as can be. Finally, I couldn't hold it in anymore. "Listen, I got a letter from Harvard. I got kicked out. They said my acceptance was a mistake." And my dad said, "Well, I guess you'll have to find someplace else to go next semester."

I stewed about it inside all weekend, feeling terrible. On Monday, my dad told me the whole thing was a prank. He wrote the letter. I totally fell for it. But he was a master practical joker. My dad would always giggle when he pulled a joke, so even though I was mad, I couldn't stay mad at him.

After four years in crimson, with that Harvard diploma safely tucked away, Kris decided to stick close to home and attend medical school at Boston University.

MEDICAL SCHOOL

One of your first classes in medical school is Gross Anatomy. You spend the year examining and dissecting a cadaver—somebody who left their body to a medical school for students to study, which is a pretty generous thing to do. Groups of students are assigned one body for the entire year. Some of the guys in my group were so naïve that they didn't realize our cadaver was a female until we got to the pelvic section. She'd had a double mastectomy, and they just didn't figure it out. Nobody dated any of those guys!

Someday gross anatomy will probably be virtual, done on computers, which is too bad because there's really no experience like learning human anatomy first hand. I still remember the horrible formaldehyde smell of the lab, all the bodies wrapped up. For anatomy exams, you'd go from body to body in the lab identifying different body parts, answering questions. Sometimes they'd sneak a bison femur or something into our final exam to see if anybody would spot it.

For Kris and her fellow med students, even when it was work, it wasn't all work. There were some perks to being a medical student in Boston.

One of our surgical rotations was a one-month rotation at Cape Cod Hospital, a community hospital in Hyannis. They even had a house for the medical students to live in. That was a big deal. You got to rotate on a busy surgical service and spend a month on Cape Cod—and if you played your cards right you got to do all this during a summer month. It was a lot of fun, but it was also pretty damn hard work.

It was at Cape Cod Hospital where Kris experienced the moment of truth that happens to every medical student, the moment when you have to prove you're actually capable of delivering medical care to a patient.

I was in the plastic surgery room when the surgeon, Dr. Robert Yoo, handed me the needle driver to do a subcuticular (beneath the skin) *skin closure. I had never put a stitch in anyone before. This was one of my first rotations, and I thought, "God, I don't know if I can do this. I'm supposed to be a surgeon, and what if I can't even put a skin stitch in?" This was a plastic surgery case, on a woman's face, and I was thinking, "God, I can't screw this up." But it went perfectly.*

There's a saying of Ben Franklin's: "Tell me and I may forget. Teach me and I may remember. Involve me and I will learn." When you're a student, and you love what you do, it's very apparent to those who are trying to teach you. You can sit here all day long watching surgery, but until someone hands you the needle driver to put a stitch in, you'll never really understand.

One of the objectives of medical school training is to help students choose a career path. There's no one, general doctor role. There are medical people (whose job title usually ends in "...gist") who diagnose, and surgeons, who fix what the medical people diagnose.

We say the medical people just like to spend all day talking about the patient, and they say surgeons are just technicians who fix stuff. The truth is we need each other. I always took my medical rotations very seriously. To be the best surgeon, I had to be the best physician. I was much more the doer and fixer, although my H&Ps (History & Physical) *were noted for their thoroughness. I'd wind up including the histories of all of the patient's extended-family members, I'd find out their pet's names, I'd make sure they weren't Yankee fans. I was very detail-oriented. I got all the information, necessary or not.*

Part of the medical career decision-making process is to put medical students into as many different environments in as short a time as possible. The amount of information thrown at medical students is daunting, but there is wisdom to the winnowing-out process.

In medical school, you rotate through lots of different specialties: internal medicine, OB/GYN, psychiatry, pediatrics, surgery, and sub-specialties that you get to choose. And whatever rotation I was doing I'd think, "This is what I'm going to do." My first delivery on my OB/GYN rotation, the baby grabbed my finger and I said, "That's it, I'm going into obstetrics." I was fascinated by some aspect of every rotation. All of them except psychiatry. That's the only one I really didn't like, because quite honestly I thought most of the psychiatrists were crazier than the patients.

One of the surgical disciplines that fascinated Kris in medical school was plastic surgery. Not the "nip & tuck" kind that jumps out at you from the pages of *People* magazine, but from a deeper, more historical context.

Plastic surgery was one of the first surgical disciplines. It goes back to the wars in ancient Greece and Rome. If your nose got cut off by a sword in battle, they needed people who could put it back on. I was interested in plastic surgery because it was very creative. My mother had a friend who knew a plastic surgeon in Boston, Dr. Julian Pribaz, an excellent plastic-reconstructive surgeon. So, I picked up the phone and called him and said, "I'm really interested in plastic surgery. Do you think I could shadow you?"

That resulted in a rotation on the Plastic and Reconstructive Surgery service at Brigham and Women's Hospital in Boston, seeing and doing all kinds of things. There were so many incredible cases. One was an arm reimplantation—nerves, arteries, veins, bone, muscles—on a guy who punched his fist through a glass wall. It was an 18-hour surgery performed by Dr. Charlie Hergrueter. I was fascinated. I stayed in the OR the entire time. Never took a break. Then there was a complex penile reconstruction for a patient who had a chronic, indwelling Foley catheter for a neurogenic bladder—his bladder malfunctioned due to nerve damage from an accident that left him paralyzed. We did complex breast reconstructions after mastectomy for cancer, extensive skin grafts for whole body burns, and the occasional nose job. It was great.

The confidence with which Dr. G approaches her work today began to blossom in Kris, the med student.

I applied for a surgical rotation with Dr. Blake Cady, an oncologic surgeon at the Deaconess Hospital in Boston. It's now called Beth Israel Deaconess Hospital. I was in the OR with the chief resident and we were dissecting through the abdominal wall. Dr. Cady pointed at a blood vessel and asked me what it was. I told him it was the superficial epigastric artery. Dr. Cady asked the chief resident if I was correct, and the resident said I was. But I wasn't sure, so I went home that night and I looked it up in my Netter Anatomy book, which I still have here, and I realized I was wrong, it was the superior epigastric artery. So, the next day I went in to Dr. Cady and said, "Yesterday, you asked me a question and I gave you an answer. I was wrong." He looked at me and said, "You're going to be a great surgeon. Because when you gave me your answer, you said it with such confidence that no one was going to question you. Very nice."

From that point on, Kris decided it would be best to be both confident and correct whenever possible.

Internship, and increasing levels of responsibility excited the young woman who, now that she had graduated from medical school, could officially be called "doctor."

INTERNSHIP

I did my internship at Brown University Hospital, in Providence, Rhode Island. As the intern, you're always the first one to be called down to the E.R., usually for abdominal pain. And we all want it to be penetrating chest trauma so we can crack the chest in the emergency room, because opening a chest and doing open cardiac massage—what's cooler than that? I didn't want the drunk throwing up on me, or the burn patient. We had all that stuff, but that's not what you want. The emergency department thoracotomy (surgical incision of the side of the chest)*—that's it! The outcomes usually weren't great because you only open chests when a patient comes in close to dead. If they lost vital signs en route, within a minute or two of the E.R., you might still try. Or, if they lost their vitals right in front of you, then you could crack the chest. But if they lost vitals out in the field and it was a long time getting to the E.R., opening the chest wasn't going to do any good.*

It's not all glamour when you're an intern. There's a lot of what medical people call "scut" work, which is a polite way of saying, "This is a job nobody else wants to do. You're the new kid. Do it."

You always get scutted out as the intern, but at the time you're doing the work it doesn't seem that way. A call goes out: "Hey, we need someone to come hold the heart." I was always the first one there. You didn't realize you were being scutted out. You were feeling like it was this great honor to come and hold the heart. And then you think, "I'm holding the heart. It's freezing cold. My hands and my fingers are going to fall off, and I have to stay still so they can sew the coronaries on this thing." But still, you're holding a human heart in your hands. There's nothing that can compare to that. I was hooked.

Dr. G's intern days were over 20 years ago, but looking back on them is like climbing into a time machine, and when she talks about them now, the years melt away.

You could have made a movie about us: "The Internship." My internship was fabulous. I don't see all my co-interns that often, but I think of them as if I was just with them yesterday. Dr. Christine Haugen, Dr. Rob Catania, Dr. Chris Nessel, Dr. Matt Davis, Dr. Joe Lifrak, Dr. Leslie Tackett, Dr. Ray Harshbarger, Dr. Steve Gemmett, Dr. Dave Iannitti, Dr. Jeff Slaiby, Dr. Fabio Potenti and others. Ray and Leslie also wound up in Texas by the way, working at Dell Children's Hospital in Austin.

We never stopped working. We got to work somewhere between 4:30 and 5:00 in the morning. We examined the patients, drew the labs, started IVs, and wrote the daily progress notes and then, finally, went to the operating room. We did everything. And somehow we still managed to meet up at the end of the day and go out and have dinner and drinks. I don't know how we did it. We just bonded. We spent literally morning, noon, and night together. This was back in the days where you were "in-house" when you were on call. You stayed over at the hospital. But, there were also days when whoever was free, we'd just get up and go. Not just the interns but the residents, too. Dr. Steve Gemmett, Dr. David Iannitti, Dr. Jeff Slaivy, and Dr. Fabio Potenti. We'd go down to the Narragansett, jump on a boat, go water skiing, catch a couple of fish, grill on the back of a boat, drink your beer and wine, and then you were back at work at 4:30 the next morning. Those were great times.

Every rung up the medical ladder means increases in responsibility, patient care, and hours worked.

RESIDENCY

Residency, and Dr. G continued to make her own breaks.

You want to know what's it's like to do lots of different types of surgery, and see if that's an area that you want to pursue. But the problem is that there are only 12 months in the year. You have some mandatory rotations, so you can't experience everything. But you can just hang out around the OR, and when you've got time, and there's something cool going on somewhere, you say, "Hey, can I come in?" So, that's how I got exposure to surgery, and gravitated toward it. It was creative, and I loved that.

I really loved vascular surgery because the patients were very sick, and the surgical procedures had to be very technically precise. We would revascularize (restore circulation to a compromised body part) *diabetics who had atherosclerotic disease* (dangerous buildup of plaque within arteries) *involving the arterial vessels in their legs, trying to re-establish blood flow to the foot—and you knew how successful you were right away. They'd come in with their foot freezing cold, pale white, sometimes they had lost motor function; they couldn't move it because they no longer had good blood supply. They'd have gangrenous toes and infected feet. But man, when you got a pulse down there and you felt that foot warm up and it turned red—you knew you did something good. You didn't have to wait to see if the chemo was working or not. For me, that quick result was really satisfying. I'm like that in other ways, too. Even when I'm cooking, I prefer to cook on the burner or out on the grill. I like to bake, but with baking you have to wait to see if it turned out right. But if I'm sautéing something, tasting it as I go, adding a little more this or that, I can tweak it the way I like it and know if it's good right away.*

The increased responsibility of residency becomes apparent when a young doctor finds herself being given a much larger share of patient care. There were still senior doctors looking over Dr. G's shoulder, but now it was in the operating room.

I've been very lucky to have many people in my life who have influenced me in a very positive way. Dr. Bill Cioffi was a great influence. He was my general surgery program director, and is now Chief of Surgery at Brown. He believed in molding you into a leader. Cioffi, as we all called him, is a tough guy. But he taught me one of the most important lessons of my surgical career when I was a resident, and that's to take ownership of the patient—it's my patient, I'm the captain of the ship, I'm responsible. Unless you have that ingrained into your brain early on, you won't be a good surgeon. It wasn't long before I thought these patients' lives were 100 percent in my hands, and if I screwed something up—if there was any kind of problem, it was 100 percent my fault. I didn't grasp that there was this multiple layer of people before anyone would be pointing a finger at me. I just thought, "If I don't do this, this patient isn't going to survive." And that's continued to today. Now, as the attending surgeon, the surgeon in charge of the case, if I get the sense that people aren't engaging in the care of patients as well as they should be, I'm going to be on top of it. I'm always double-checking, I'm trying to make sure that I have a hold of what's going on with them.

Cioffi was also good about reining you in when you didn't do a good job with something. It was always a positive critique, never punitive. Cioffi was probably one of the greatest mentors in my general surgical training, and I still keep in touch him with today.

One of the benchmarks of surgical residency comes when a special piece of equipment is finally bestowed on the young doctor.

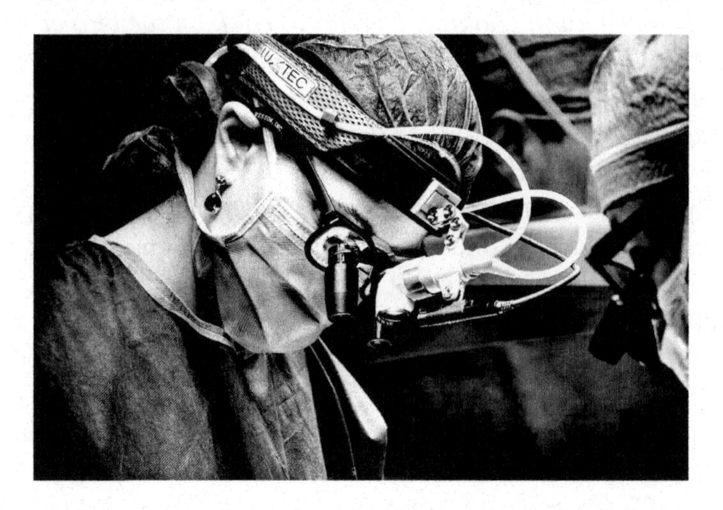

It was a rite of passage when you got to be a second-year resident—you got your surgical loupes, the magnifying glasses that enlarge the surgical field you're looking at. They were 2.5x—two-and-a-half magnification. I still use those now for some cases, but usually I have 3.5x, or 4.5x for some of the little, less than two-kilogram babies.

When I was a third-year general surgery resident I spent some time on the Cardiothoracic Surgery service at Brown. One day I was in the operating room with one of the heart surgeons at Brown, Dr. George Cooper. I was helping him with a coronary artery bypass operation, and I had my surgical loupes on. Traditionally, the surgical residents didn't get to do anything for heart cases because we weren't cardiac residents. In fact, they didn't even have cardiac surgery residents at Brown. But for whatever reason, that day I got to help. At that time, we would take the patient's saphenous vein (the longest vein in the body, running the length of the lower leg) *to use as conduits for coronary artery bypass grafting. I was up in the field with Dr. Cooper as his first assistant and he handed me the needle driver and told me to do the distal anastomosis* (surgical connection of two structures). *Now, of the two anastomoses, the proximal* (bigger and easier connection) *and the distal* (smaller, more technically challenging), *the distal is the harder one. Typically, if a general surgery resident ever got to do anything in the very beginning, it might be the proximal. He let me do a distal. I'd never done a coronary anastomosis, and I was excited, but a bit nervous. But, I took the needle driver from him as if I did it every day, and I put every stitch in place to complete the anastomosis, and I tied it down, waited a bit and saw (fingers crossed) that it didn't leak. Then I looked up and said, "Could someone please call my parents and tell them what I just did?" And the patient lived, which is important.*

Even in the enlightened medical community, Dr. G still found people willing to—at least metaphorically—stand in her way.

When I was in residency, I told one surgeon I planned to go into cardiothoracic surgery. He just laughed and said, "You'll just quit surgery and just go home and have babies." He was a real jerk, and a terrible surgeon. The big thing that's changed is that people today are better at not saying things out loud so often. Although, even today, if I tell someone I work at Children's Medical Center they'll say, "Oh, are you a nurse?" Sometimes, I think all we've really done is raise the glass ceiling to a higher level. But I know we're making strides. We just have to keep it up.

What's amazing is that you have to make all these important career decisions when you're very young. You're in your twenties, you have energy, you don't think you ever need to sleep. And if you are on call every other night? Well, all that means is you're going to miss fifty percent of the interesting cases. The big rule they told us as residents was, "Eat when you can, sleep when you can—and don't mess with the pancreas." That last part was because operating on the pancreas is notorious for a bad outcome.

As her time at Brown drew to a close, Dr. G was faced with another of the fork-in-the-road moments young doctors continually face. Dr. Cioffi was suggesting she consider a trauma fellowship. Dr. Kirby Bland, the Chief of Surgery and a world-renowned oncologic surgeon, suggested to Dr. G that she follow in his footsteps. She'd spent a good deal of time in both of those fields and they interested her, but they didn't stir her passions the way cardiac surgery did.

Research is traditionally done after a resident's second clinical year, but for various reasons, that plan didn't work out for Dr. G. The only time it was feasible for her to do research was after her term as Chief Resident at Brown. One Surgical Grand Rounds session at Brown particularly intrigued Dr. G. She listened to her senior resident, Dr. Chris Breuer, back from his research fellowship, recounting his experience in cardiovascular tissue engineering with Drs. Jay Vacanti and John Mayer at Children's Hospital Boston. A light went on in her head just as it had years before when the young Kris listened to Dr. Tenley Albright, and she took a new direction. She finished her general surgical residency at Brown and returned to her hometown, to take part in cutting-edge research under the direction of Dr. Mayer.

RESEARCH FELLOW

I was now 30 years old, working on bioengineering—tissue-engineering heart valves. When a baby is born with a congenital heart defect that requires valve replacement, the only available valves are those from cadavers. The tissue is dead so the valve can't grow as the child grows. It's inevitable that they will need a replacement, or likely multiple replacements, over the years. The tissue-engineering approach is really a marriage between biology and engineering. The goal was to grow valves made of one's own tissue that could be implanted and theoretically grow as the patient grows, to eliminate the need for those repeated surgeries. There was already a lamb model for this research, but I wanted to try it with human tissue. I thought that a good potential source of cells might be circulating progenitor cells from discarded umbilical cords left over from C-sections. Brigham & Women's Hospital was right next door so, after establishing a protocol, I started collecting samples to use in parallel with our lamb studies.

The lamb studies entailed collecting circulating progenitor cells from pregnant lambs at about halfway through gestation and growing those cells in an incubator, seeding them onto a biodegradable construct and then after delivery of the lambs implanting the tissue-engineered valves into the lamb. The cool part was that since about 75% of lamb gestations are twins, I had a subject and a control.

I had never done fetal surgery before, only read about it. My fellowship was ending just as we were getting into the clinical part of the trial, but we had grown some valves and implanted them, and all of the lambs survived. I was pleasantly surprised. Ironically it was Dr. Joe Forbess, a junior faculty member in the Department of Cardiovascular Surgery, and my future surgical partner at Children's Medical Center, who helped me sew in the first valve.

It was during this fellowship that Dr. G encountered one of the most important mentors she would ever have.

Dr. Judah Folkman was one of the most amazing people I've ever met. He was a pediatric general surgeon by training, but a scientist in the truest form of the word. His research focus was on angiogenesis (the formation of new blood vessels) *and its relation to tumor growth. He developed angiogenesis inhibitors, drugs to prevent the formation of new blood vessels. The concept was that angiogenesis inhibitors would inhibit the blood supply that feeds tumors, possibly a cure for cancer. He cured cancer in laboratory mice. This guy was brilliant, and every talk he gave was so inspiring. But what I learned from him was less about the science and more about the person. Every time he went to Surgical Grand Rounds he would always sit in the front row of the auditorium. The topic could be something he had no background or interest in, but he always had questions—pertinent ones. He was the big cheese, but his hand was always up. I admired that because he never considered himself above anybody. He'd never say "I'm too smart for that, I'm too good for that." He listened intently to everybody. It could be an intern, a new lab fellow, or a world-renowned researcher giving a talk. He was always there, always front and center, always paying attention, and always asking the most insightful questions.*

Dr. Folkman didn't buy into the hierarchy of things. He looked at everyone on equal grounds. He'd say, "You know, everybody in the research lab wants to do award-winning research, right? They want to win the Nobel Prize. In my lab, we had all sorts of possible research projects on a pin board. But all the PhD candidates wanted to come up with their own idea so that they could own it and be the senior author on it. Even though all these ideas were posted on the door, everyone would say, 'Oh no, no. I've got my own idea.' Then, a new research fellow came in and said he really didn't have any ideas of his own. So, he took an idea off the board and worked with it. His first three papers were published in three of the most prestigious medical journals, Nature, Science, and Cell."

The point is, Dr. Folkman believed in everybody. He taught me things about leadership that I use in my thinking process every day. And directly or indirectly, he instilled in me the proper way to lead others. He taught me that some leaders stay on top by making themselves "King of the hill," never allowing those around you to outdo you, so you're always safe. Others are the type that surround themselves with the A-team, people who they allow to blossom, and bring up the whole team. He always said, "For me, the definition of success is not looking at what I've been able to achieve, but what those around me have been able to achieve. That is the greatest satisfaction."

THORACIC RESIDENCY

When it was time for her thoracic surgery residency, Dr. G found herself leaving New England for the very first time. Her mother accompanied her to St. Louis to help get her acclimated to her new setting as she began the next step in her training at Barnes Hospital/Washington University School of Medicine, with rotations at Barnes-Jewish Hospital and St. Louis Children's Hospital.

We were at the grocery store, stocking up for my new apartment. (My mother will deny this, but I swear it's a true story.) We were walking around the produce section and she turned to me and said, "Oh, honey, look! They have the same kinds of fruits and vegetables we have back in Boston." It was hilarious. She'll kill me when she reads this.

Dr. G was now on track to become a cardiothoracic surgeon, which means operating on the heart, the lungs, the esophagus—anything inside the thoracic cavity. As she focused on her chosen specialty, another mentor appeared.

When I got to St. Louis I started on the General Thoracic Service and one of the first people I came across, another one of my mentors and role models to this day, was Dr. Alec Patterson, one of the world's most accomplished thoracic surgeons, particularly in the field of lung transplantation. He performed the world's first double lung transplant. He's one of those people who is always positive. If you felt like you couldn't do something, or if you had any doubt about your capabilities, he would just push you, and build you up, and make you feel like you could do it. And you would. As opposed to other people I've worked with over the years that don't do that. In fact, they do just the opposite. They push you down, make you doubt yourself and, as a result, you lose confidence. One of the biggest challenges in this field is that you can be a technically excellent surgeon, smart as a whip. But if you lose belief in yourself, if there's any self-doubt about what you can or can't do—well, that's the kiss of death.

For a big sports fan like Dr. G, St. Louis was a great place to live and work.

I operated on Jack Buck, the voice of the St. Louis Cardinals. All these famous Cardinals players would come to visit him; Stan Musial, Ozzie Smith. I got to meet them all. My very first patient was the wife of Conrad Dobler, who played for the football Cardinals. I had been told that everybody in the Midwest was bigger, and here I walk into this room filled with Dobler, Dan Dierdorf, Jim Hart, other NFL players—all five feet of me. I thought, "Wow, they do grow them big here."

My first month was incredibly busy. My senior fellow, Dr. Steve Cassivi, called me the night before I started and he told me his wife had just gone into labor, so he wouldn't be there to orient me. I'd have to run the service alone. He just said, "Good luck. You'll be fine." Now, the thoracic surgery service at Wash. U. was one of the busiest in the country at the time. In my first eight days, I performed enough esophageal surgery cases to fulfill my American Board of Thoracic Surgery requirement, something that can take six months to achieve. I also did eleven double lung transplants that first month. It was crazy busy. We were even helping out when we were not on call.

I was in a group session with Dr. Joel Cooper, chief of cardiothoracic surgery at Barnes, talking about diseases. He asked us if anybody knew the formal name for "Coal Miner's disease." So, I piped up and said, "Yes, it's 'pneumonoultramicroscopicsilicovolcanoconiosis,' the longest word in the English language, 45 letters and 19 syllables." He just looked at me and said, "OK, little Miss Smarty Pants!" I didn't tell him the reason I knew it is because it was one of my spelling words in third grade. (If you want to try it, here's the pronunciation—pneu·mo·no·ul·tra·mi·cro·scop·ic·sil·i·co·vol·ca·no·co·ni·o·sis.)

Dr. G began to find her stride in St. Louis. Fortunately for her, she already had the footwear to stride in.

One night I went out on an organ procurement wearing four-inch Prada heels which I wore to dinner, thinking my clogs would be at the hospital. But they weren't. Usually, one team goes on the procurement and then another team does the transplant. So, I figured I was only going to retrieve the lungs, drop them off in the OR, and then go home. But when I got back, Dr. Patterson said, "You're welcome to stay and sew in the lungs." Of course, I stayed. It was always a blast to operate with Dr. Patterson. At the end of the night, after about ten hours of surgery, someone said, "You operated in high heels?" and I said, "If you can't operate in heels, you can't operate."

CHAPTER SEVEN

Waiting

"This is the case that's gonna drive me out of surgery."

"Am I watching my child die before my eyes?"

Andrea and Gilly Riojas were haunted by that thought as they sat with their brave, frail, two-year-old girl in the pale green light of their CVICU room. Nothing about Rylynn's entire childhood to date was normal. She had a large machine attached to her failing heart. Just getting her out of bed took coordinated movements to position her so that the cannulae inserted into her abdomen would not rub harshly against her skin and cause her discomfort. A walk around the ICU, which would take an adult all of 90 seconds, was a ten-minute journey for Rylynn, a nurse in front of her wheeling the Berlin Heart pumping mechanism.

Rylynn alternated between alert and listless in the days following the Berlin Heart implantation, running fevers and experiencing sores around the placement of the cannula on her right side. Her antibody levels were already high. Following the VAD surgery and several blood transfusions, they had gone even higher. Her latest PRAs meant that only around ten percent of potential donor hearts might be a good match for her. She began to have even more trouble sleeping, which can be deadly, as sleep is essential for ICU patients. Andrea decided to keep track of the sleep meds that her daughter was given for just one night:

9:00 PM	Ambien (sleeping medication)
12:30 AM	Ativan (anti-anxiety)
2:00 AM	Morphine (narcotic painkiller)
4:00 AM	Benadryl (antihistamine)
5:00 AM	Ativan (double dose)

This dosing would probably put an adult out for days, but Rylynn kept waking up every five to 15 minutes.

The doctors continued making a series of moves in the chess game they were helping Rylynn play against nature, and against time. She went back to the cath lab less than a month after the VAD implantation so doctors could figure out why her heart pressures were so high, and why fluid was accumulating in her lungs. A stent was placed in her left pulmonary artery, enlarging it to help with blood flow to the lungs and reduce the pressure the right ventricle was pumping against. A series of coils was inserted along Rylynn's malformed heart, to remove some of the collateral arteries that had developed as her heart actually tried to repair itself.

Toward the end of August, Rylynn stabilized to the point where she could leave the CVICU and move back up to the 8th floor Cardiology Ward. This thrilled her parents, who now would have a private bathroom with shower, and be allowed to eat and drink in their daughter's room. After the move upstairs Andrea noticed a certain, if predictable, change had come over her two-year-old.

"She started to just yell 'NO' at everybody who came into her room, and she screamed and fought. Everybody at the hospital kept telling us that this was normal. She had no control over her body, her room, anything in her life. This was her way of telling us she was just fed up with it all."

The turn to September meant Texas A&M football, a Riojas family passion. It also brought Rylynn closer to death than she'd ever been. When her kidneys began to fail on September 6th, she was moved back to the CVICU. This was an ominous sign. Rylynn's heart was no longer doing enough work to keep her other organs alive, even with the VAD. There had been few good organ offers for her. A nephrologist wanted to take Rylynn into the OR immediately. Her potassium was dangerously elevated, to a level that might induce cardiac arrest in an adult. Hoping the VAD would help Rylynn overcome the kidney problems, Andrea and Gilly decided to wait. Later that night, they were delighted to find a wet diaper, a sign that kidney problem was lessening.

Things went south again two days later. Andrea noticed Rylynn was having trouble putting any weight on her right leg. A head ultrasound and CT-scan were ordered. A neurologist came to Rylynn's ICU room late that afternoon and said to Andrea, "Well, I guess you heard the results of the scan. We found some evidence of a stroke."

Andrea had not heard, and the news hit her like a thunderbolt. "Stroke" is a terrifying word, especially in an ICU setting. The danger of stroke had been discussed at length before the Berlin Heart procedure. Rylynn had to be put on high levels of anticoagulants to prevent clots from occurring. It's a common problem with VADs. Small particles and strings of particles form in the cannula, and occasionally one will break off and enter the patient's circulatory system. The theory was that a small particle had come loose and lodged in the right frontal lobe of Rylynn's brain. Normally, an MRI would be ordered for a detailed look at the brain, but MRIs were out of the question for a patient connected to a large, metal machine.

Andrea was on top of her daughter's situation all the time, continually proactive on her behalf. She had done her homework and knew what questions to ask.

"I spent the next couple of days driving the nurses crazy with questions. Will her leg get back to normal? Are we at more of a risk for stroke now? Do other VAD kids have strokes?"

Dr. G decided it was time to switch the pump on Rylynn's Berlin Heart to a new unit free of fibrin. This was a much simpler job than the original implantation, and it only required about a minute of disconnect from the machine, with no invasive procedures. During the time off the assist device, Rylynn's heart pumped naturally, on its own. But she began to suffer even more alarming fluid buildup throughout her body when her kidney problem didn't abate. It was at this point that Dr. G decided further surgical intervention was needed.

Rylynn's kidneys started failing, and her belly got very distended. She had accumulated a lot of fluid in her abdomen. She was beginning to develop what we call abdominal compartment syndrome—the increased pressure from the fluid presses on everything and makes it more difficult for the internal organs to function. If we could release that pressure on the abdomen, it would allow more blood flow to get to the kidneys and promote more urine output.

I asked one of our general surgeons to put a PD (peritoneal dialysis) *catheter in her. He just shook his head and said, "No way. It's not worth it. She looks like she's dying." I begged him, and finally, he did it.*

"The night when they decided to put in the PD catheter, Dr. G came into our room," Andrea said, "and she told us what was going to happen and why, and it got kind of emotional. She hugged us both, and we cried a little bit."

I dropped in on Dr. G in her office one September day during these extreme up and down moments with Rylynn. She was looking at reports of potential donor hearts from the UNOS computer, shaking her head. She said if she couldn't find a heart for Rylynn, this would be the case that would drive her out of surgery. It was the only negative comment I ever heard her utter about her work.

The good news was the PD catheter did the trick, draining off large amounts of fluid, reducing the swelling that made it difficult for Rylynn to even move her arms or legs, and her kidneys began to function more normally than they had in some time. But she was still intubated and sedated, so it was difficult to gauge how much she'd recovered. Andrea and Gilly were told Rylynn might have to remain on a ventilator for at least a couple of weeks if she wasn't strong enough to breathe on her own. The possibility of a quick donor match could not be discounted; however, given her antibody problems, a lengthy wait seemed much more probable.

Rylynn proved her usual, resilient self, able to come off the ventilator quickly. But two nights later, after a trip to the lobby in her stroller, the two-year-old grabbed her head and began screaming. Minutes later, she threw up. A CT-scan was ordered to make sure there was no bleeding in her brain. By the time they returned from radiology to CVICU, she was feeling better. The nurses took blood and urine samples, as well as a sample from her PD cath. She had an infection in her abdomen. This bit of bad news also put a temporary hold on her transplant eligibility. She would remain off the list until the problem was resolved. Fortunately, Rylynn's infection was gone in two days, and she was restored to 1A status, the top of the transplant list. The waiting began once again.

Life for a parent in the CVICU is always difficult. Andrea's life had settled into an almost mind-numbing routine.

"I always had breakfast after my shower at 6:00 AM," Andrea said. "I took three flights of stairs down to the cafeteria and got a muffin and coffee, then took three flights back up. I ate in the waiting room and was back in Rylynn's room by 7:00 AM rounds—every single day. That was the one hour each day I left that room. Otherwise I was there 23 hours a day. In fact, for 4 months, I didn't even have a car. I never left. Each weekend when Gilly came, he brought us dinner and we would either sneak it in the CVICU room and eat, or take turns going into the waiting area and eating. That was always wonderful! At first we tried to sit down together and eat, but Ry wouldn't have that. Just as we'd start to eat, we'd get a call from our nurse that she was asking for us. It was easier to take turns and make sure we were always at her side."

Dr. G walked into Rylynn's CVICU room on the night of October 5th, and asked Andrea what her plan for the evening was. Andrea said she was going to wash Rylynn's hair, which was always something of a chore.

Dr. G nodded and said, "OK, that's good. Well, after you're done with all that, how'd you like to get a new heart?"

CHAPTER EIGHT

Fenway Park and Cardiac Karma – Part 2

"If you get better soon,
we could head to Fenway and see a game!"

Dr. G and Andrew Madden met face-to-face in an 8th floor hallway of Children's Medical Center.

There he was, this skinny little kid with an iPod, so into his music he didn't notice anything around him. He was wearing a red t-shirt that said "Tornadoes," which was the name of his Little League team. He was a little startled when I walked up to him. I introduced myself and told him that I heard he liked baseball. I said, "Well, you know I'm from Boston, and I'm a huge Red Sox fan." He was pale as a ghost, skinny as could be—but his eyes just lit up and he said, "The Red Sox are my favorite team!" When I asked him why he said, "Well, because they're the underdog a lot of the time and I love that. And in 2004 when they won the World Series it was such a great comeback." We bonded right there.

Andrew was diagnosed with his heart condition at birth, so he was used to being around doctors. Even though he was obviously scared and nervous, he was very cooperative and realistic, a team player. Whenever I saw him on rounds, before we talked about any medical stuff first we always talked about what was up with the Red Sox. I was rounding on a Friday afternoon and I noticed he was on his laptop, so I asked him what he was doing. He said he had to order a new Red Sox cap because he'd left his at home in Odessa. I told him to hold off. What I didn't tell him was that my family back in Boston had just sent me a package full of Red Sox gear including the traditional blue cap with the red "B" on it. So, the next morning on rounds, I gave him a little gift box with the Red Sox cap in it and I put a note in that said, "Here's a little something for good luck. The Best Is Yet to Come! Love, Dr. G." He opened the box, got a huge smile on his face, put the cap on and asked if it would be OK to wear the cap during his transplant. I told him of course he could, and I'd wear my Red Sox OR cap—because with the Red Sox, it's all about the karma.

Red Sox karma kicked in—the trading of Babe Ruth to the Yankees; the ball skipping under Bill Buckner's glove; 86 years between World Series wins—all things that give rise to that perseverance Red Sox fans display through the tough times. Their shared love of baseball provided a needed diversion during one of the most difficult parts of the transplant process. In sports, one team loses and one team wins. For Andrew to go on living, somebody else had to die. And not just die, but die in a certain manner.

Not every donor heart is suitable for transplantation. First and foremost, the heart function has to be normal. Then, there are both absolute and relative contraindications based on the donor's medical and social history, circumstances of death, and any means of resuscitation, and supportive medications that might have been employed.

During the wait for a heart for Andrew, despite a schedule full of surgeries, consults, teaching, and conferences, Dr. G decided to take on a rare social engagement.

Two of the cardiologists at the hospital, Dr. Reenu Eapen and Dr. Vivian Dimas, were pregnant. I offered to host a double baby shower for them at my house, even though I was on call that entire weekend. The invitations were already sent out. Guests would arrive Sunday at noon. I'd done all the food shopping the day before, picked up the flowers. Now some people might say I'm a type A, but the only way I would do it was to do it all myself. Somehow, between rounds early Sunday morning and the shower at noon, I knew I could make the tea sandwiches, no crusts, of course, I'd be able to prepare the smoked salmon, the capers, the chopped eggs, crème fraiche, chives, and a bit of caviar. I'd have the gorgonzola, prosciutto and fig hors d'oeuvres prepared—everything. I was going to start preparing everything at 9:00 am on Sunday. But of course, Sunday morning at 4:00, my pager went off—a donor heart offer for Andrew. It was a 24-year-old woman who had just given birth and died days after delivery. A young, healthy woman with the right blood type, a perfect match. And it was right next door at Parkland Hospital, so there'd be no long trip to procure the donor heart. I had so much going through my mind. I was excited for Andrew. At the same time, I was heartbroken for the donor family—the new baby who would never have a mother —but what I know all too well is that every transplant story has to involve a tragedy.

Since I was already awake at four in the morning, I thought I'd start preparing the food for the baby shower while organizing the transplant with the coordinator. I put up sticky notes all over the house about what needed to go where and how to make the last-minute preparations. I got it all set up—flowers arranged, gifts wrapped, table set, champagne chilled—and then I went to Children's to do the transplant. Just before the surgery began I called one of my friends and explained to her I couldn't be there for the shower, but I told her where I hid my house key so she could go in and run everything. I told her everything was all set, and to have a great time, and to not forget the salmon in the refrigerator. When the shower got going and they knew I was in surgery, one of them called into OR-6 to ask me where I kept my fire extinguisher. It took me a moment to realize they were just kidding.

Andrew's surgery would be the 100th heart transplant performed at Children's Medical Center. In honor of this milestone, Dr. G decided to invite Dr. W. Steves Ring to assist her. Dr. Ring performed the first heart transplant at Children's, in 1988, and was Department Chairman of Cardiothoracic Surgery for 22 years.

Dr. Ring was my department chairman when I started here, so I thought it would be only fitting to invite him to assist me since it was the 100th transplant, and he said he'd be honored. And because it was the 100th, the local media got involved. As we agreed, I was *wearing my Red Sox OR cap, and Andrew had his new Red Sox baseball cap. Karma. The reporters who were covering the transplant were confused about why, at Children's Medical Center in Dallas, the two of us had on Boston Red Sox caps. I explained I was from Boston, I love the Red Sox, and Andrew was also a big Red Sox fan. So, that's how the story became public. After that it just spiraled out of control and had a life of its own.*

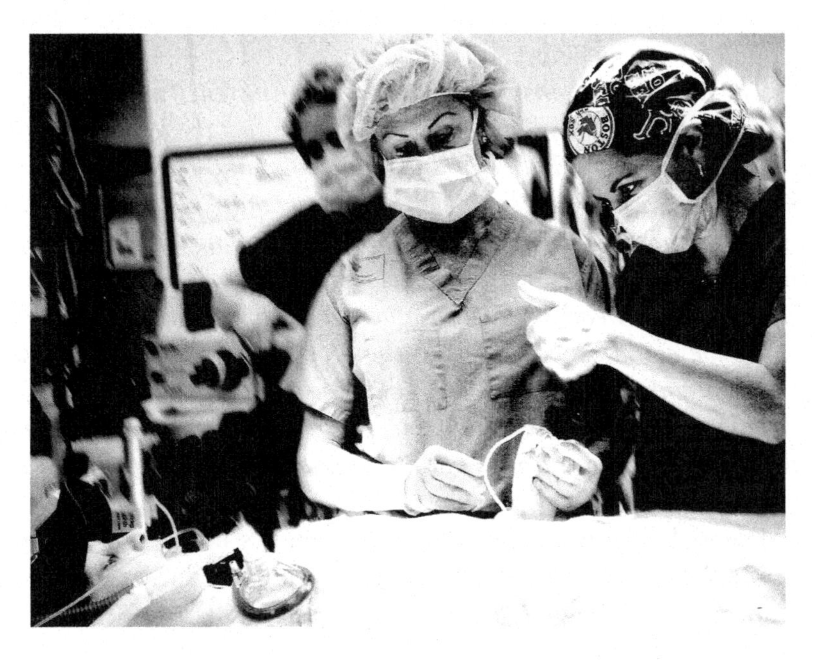

Red Sox Karma - Dr. G gives Andrew Madden thumbs up before his transplant in 2007 as OR nurse Lyn Culbertson looks on. (photo by Lou Curtis, courtesy Children's Medical Center)

It was a fairly routine operation for what the official surgical report calls "Orthotopic Cardiac Transplantation." The donor heart was en route to the OR from nearby Parkland Hospital. Andrew's chest was cut open and his breastbone spread apart with a retractor. Cannulae were placed in the aorta and vena cavae to route his blood into the heart-lung bypass machine for oxygenation, and then back into his body to recirculate. Dr. G clamped Andrew's aorta, removed his heart and put it aside for later examination by pathologists. Five vascular connections were completed, implanting the donor heart. The aortic cross clamp was released, the perfusionist warmed Andrew's blood on pump, and the young woman's heart began to beat in his body. The entire procedure had taken over ten hours, with Dr. G focused on Andrew's open chest for six hours straight with no breaks. Andrew's surgery was a slam-dunk for Dr. G when compared to the transplant she had performed just a couple of weeks before.

The little guy I transplanted just before Andrew was our youngest, tiniest heart transplant recipient ever—in fact the world's smallest at the time—barely five pounds in weight, and barely one week old. While that little guy was getting better and Andrew was waiting for a heart to become available, I started joking with him. "You know, my family has season tickets at Fenway. If you get better soon we could head to Boston and see a game. You never know. Maybe we could even make it to the World Series." Now, this was early September, it was still the regular season. The playoffs hadn't started yet. Nobody knew which teams would be in the Series. And more times than not, things hadn't always worked out for the Red Sox late in the season.

Events began to link unexpectedly. Dr. G's father was turning 70, and the family planned a weekend in Las Vegas during Andrew's recuperation. Though not much of a gambler, Dr. G decided to take a shot at roulette. She put $10 down on number nine—Ted Williams' number with the Red Sox and Andrew's number on his Little League team—and five dollars on red, for Red Sox. Number nine, red, hit, paying off at 33:1.

I'd never played roulette before. 33-1 odds. I couldn't believe it. If this wasn't karma, I don't know what is. I looked at my brother, and I told him I had to call Andrew and let him know. Michael said, "Do you really think it's a good idea to promote gambling to a 13-year-old?" He was right, so I filed that story away.

Right after that I flew to St. Thomas to board a cruise ship for a perfusion conference-at-sea where I'd been invited to speak. The American League Championship Series was underway by then. The

Red Sox were playing the Cleveland Indians in a best-of-seven series to see who'd be the American League team in the World Series.

While Andrew recuperated in Dallas, Dr. G boarded the ship, and her Red Sox were in trouble, trailing three games to two in the best-of-seven series. Overcoming that deficit was next to impossible.

The afternoon I got on board, even before I unpacked, I went up to the sports bar on the ship and said to one of the bartenders, "The Red Sox game will be on here tonight, right?" And he told me, no, all the TVs would all have college football on. The schedules had been set long ago. I said, "What? Nobody cares about college football now. It's October. This is the baseball playoffs! Who do I speak to? Where's the captain?"

Another guy at the bar looked over and said the Red Sox lost last night and the series was over. My heart sank. But then I thought that couldn't be right because they always had a travel day when they change cities but he said no, it was last night and that they had lost. He was so certain that I took his word for it. I was very depressed.

The next morning, Dr. G began her talk at the conference by first asking for a moment of silence for her Red Sox. She was so overwhelmed by news of her team's defeat, and wondering how Andrew was taking the loss, that after delivering her talk she went out on deck alone to read some articles on the history of cardiac surgery.

I sat there, completely broken-hearted over the Red Sox losing, but at least it would be the Indians in the World Series and not the Yankees. Then, one of the medical device reps attending the conference came over. He handed me the daily news summary they print on the cruise ship with feeds from Reuters and the New York Times. Boston had actually won game five! We were still alive!

So, there would be a game six. It was the last night of the cruise, and somehow they arranged to put our group at the Captain's table for dinner. They still didn't have the game on TV on the ship, so I called everyone in Boston to get the score—first my family, friends, trying to find somebody who was watching who could tell me how the game was going. I couldn't reach anybody. I knew they were all watching but nobody would answer my calls. Finally, I knew one person who'd be in front of his TV. I called the Ronald McDonald House in Dallas where Andrew was recuperating. He answered right away. I told him the situation and said I'd call about every 20 minutes for a score update. All during dinner I kept excusing myself, pretending to be seasick, so I could make the call. Finally, Andrew told me, "OK, Dr. G, it's 10-1 Sox." So—there would be a game seven!

I got home the next day and invited Andrew and his mother to come over for dinner and watch game seven at my house. It was a close game early, and they had to leave in the seventh inning, because Andrew was exhausted. But the Red Sox had already broken it wide open and won. They were going to the World Series!

CHAPTER NINE

Becoming a Heart Surgeon

"Those who mind don't matter,
and those who matter don't mind."

CHILDREN'S MEDICAL CENTER, DALLAS

As Dr. G began looking for her first "real job" after ten years of training it was the early part of the new century. The economy was in turmoil and jobs weren't that easy to find, certainly not in highly specialized fields of medicine.

There were only one or two jobs out there. One was in Louisville, Kentucky, and that seemed like a scary proposition—to be two plane rides away from home. I was looking back in St. Louis, where I had trained. They were trying to expand the program and create a position that would be good.

But it was Children's Medical Center in Dallas where Dr. G finally set down, through a friendship begun earlier in her career.

I met Dr. Joe Forbess when I was a research fellow in Boston. I was involved in cardiovascular tissue-engineering research, and he helped me with one of my lamb experiments.

When I was looking for jobs, I sent letters and my C.V. everywhere. And then I ran into Dr. Forbess at a critical care meeting in Miami. He had called me over the summer to ask me my thoughts about his taking a position Children's and UT Southwestern in Dallas as opposed to remaining at the Cleveland Clinic. I remember telling him, "Well, if you go to Cleveland you're going to kind of be in the shadow of Dr. Roger Mee," who's the big guy there. "And until he retires, you're not really going to be the head honcho. You're going to have to kind of do things his way. With UT Southwestern, you're it from the get go." I didn't know anything about UT Southwestern at the time, but I said it sounded like he was going to basically build a program from the ground up. But then I'm thinking, "Why is he asking me? I'm not even a full-fledged congenital heart surgeon. I'm just a fellow."

So, when I saw him at the meeting in Miami, I said, "Hey, did you ever get my application? I sent you a letter about coming to Children's to be a super-fellow," but he said he never got any letter from me.

The letter ended up getting returned to me almost a month later with a big, red stamp on the envelope—PERSON NOT FOUND. He had just started here in September, and I sent it fairly soon after that. He wasn't known to the mailroom yet. I sent it again, and he called and said, "Do you want to come down for an interview? I think you can help me as much as I'll be able to help you." So, I came for a visit. They told me it never snowed in Dallas, but it was snowing the day I arrived. I spent the day here, interviewing for hours and he said, "If you want to come and kind of be my apprentice like a super-fellow (not yet attending, but beyond a mere "fellow")*, you can do that." But then he added, "I can't guarantee that there's going to be anything after that."*

I said it sounded good, and that's how I got to Dallas and Children's Medical Center. I moved to Dallas in late March, and the weather was beautiful. I stayed at the old Melrose Hotel in the Oak Lawn section of Dallas until my apartment was ready. I went for a walk one day and I was so impressed by the incredible number of really handsome, totally buff southern gentlemen everywhere. And then, when I'd been walking for about a half-hour, I realized I hadn't seen any other women. That's when I realized I was in the gay section of town.

The job at Children's didn't start off as all glamour and glory. The endless hours of internship and residency came back in a slightly different form.

I came to Children's as a super-fellow working with Dr. Forbess, basically scrubbing every single case with him for that year, and I rounded every day for the whole year. All the while I'm thinking, "Gosh, is there going to be a job for me at the end of this?" At the end of that year, they hired me. I had my first real job at the age of 37. But there were already several surgeons here. Dr. Forbess was the division chief. Dr. Steves Ring was still operating. Drs. Hisashi Nikaidoh, Tom Yeh, and Steve Leonard were part of the division as well. There were a lot of surgeons but not enough surgical cases to spread around among seven of us. The division changed, and the personnel within the division evolved to what we have now.

It's kind of hard when you transition to being an attending surgeon in a place where you were considered a trainee—super fellow or otherwise—because most people tend to treat you as the junior surgeon forever. I knew I had to distinguish myself somehow. I was given the task of building the transplant program in early 2006. Dr. Ring started the heart transplant program at UT Southwestern in 1988, and over the past 15 years or so they had been doing a handful of heart transplants per year—a small, but growing, program. That year we started our Ventricular Assist Device Program, and immediately more than doubled our transplant volume to ten transplants that year. We've since become one of the largest, most successful and most respected pediatric heart transplant programs in the world.

Even though she's respected in her field, Dr. G is the first to admit that you can never afford to stop learning, and to always realize that there are those ahead of you to keep up with.

Even Olympic athletes have coaches. You don't just reach a certain level and then say, "Ok, I'm done being coached." I've learned as much, if not more, about what not to do and how not to be, from some of the people in charge. I never wanted to be a carbon copy of anybody. During my fellowship in Boston I worked with three surgeons: Dr. John Mayer, Dr. Pedro del Nido, and Dr. Richard Jonas. I learned different things from each of them, but I never wanted to be exactly like any of them. I wanted to be an amalgam of all of the great things that I learned from each of them. So, it was my job over the years to take the pearls— tricks, tips, and pearls—from the experts in the field to make myself a better surgeon. That's why we go to so many conferences. There are a number of outstanding congenital heart surgeons across the country who I would have loved to train with. For instance, Dr. Tom Spray is Chief of Pediatric Cardiothoracic Surgery at Children's Hospital of Philadelphia. I've never had him as a direct mentor, but I've had conversations with him, I've seen him give excellent presentations at meetings. I've learned from him and I've taken away various pearls that I use in the operating room.

Learning from other surgeons doesn't always have to take place at conferences. Sometimes, it can happen in the exam room, when you're the patient.

Part of leadership is how you deal with patients and how you want to be dealt with. I went to see an orthopedic surgeon for a problem I was having with my thumb. Now this guy is the hand guy for the Dallas Cowboys, so I figured he must be good. He was highly recommended. While he was examining my hand I told him, "You know, I need to be able to do more than just throw a ball." He didn't laugh at all. Didn't even crack a smile. I thought it was hilarious. I actually came up with that line in the waiting room. But he was serious, all business, and thankfully relayed to me that I didn't need surgery. I know he's a superstar surgeon. But I left there thinking, "Could I have a beer with this guy?"

Another time a smart doctor pays attention to detail is when a family member is sick. When you're suddenly on the other side of the equation, when you're no longer the 'expert' that everybody looks to for guidance, you get a different view of the world.

The times my father was hospitalized with his heart problems over the years were doubly tough for me. As a physician-family member, I was trying to be the daughter and not the doctor. At the same time, when it's your family member you have to speak up when you know something is potentially not right, but you don't want to be intrusive or insulting to the care team. My father was in an excellent medical system in Boston, the Harvard system, with outstanding physicians. In any teaching hospital the interns, the residents, and the fellows are coming in all the time. And even though I had been an intern, and a resident, and a fellow just like them I would think, "Do these guys know anything? They look like they're in high school!" Of course, my dad and mom would tell their physicians that I was a heart surgeon, and so people usually knew up front.

My father had a history of coronary artery disease and had been through bypass surgery and defibrillator placement. Now, he was scheduled to undergo ventricular tachycardia ablation (selectively destroying portions of the heart that generate a dangerously abnormal heart rhythm.) *I asked if they were going to do a cardiac catheterization up front and take a look at his coronary grafts, and the fellow handling the case said they weren't. I said, "Hmm. That's a bit surprising to me." Within an hour he came back and said, "Actually, yes, we are going to do that," and it was at that point that I knew that he had probably gone back to discuss everything with the attending cardiologist.*

During one of my father's hospitalizations I got a little frustrated when they couldn't find his medical records. I brought the team over and said, "OK, guys, someone is going to call his cardiologist, someone is going to call his cardiac surgeon's office, and someone is going go to Medical Records, and by the end of the day someone is going to bring me a copy of his medical records so I have them, and then you will have them as well."

I knew that he was on a beta-blocker and I noticed on his EKG tracing that he was tachycardic, so I asked if he'd gotten his beta-blocker that night. And they said, "No, we forgot." And I said, "Well, that's the reason he was admitted!" I just became a little more vocal, but—it's my dad. These were basic things, and attention to detail is something of a lost art today.

You need to be an advocate for your family member. I don't care if you're a physician or not. Today in medicine there are so many people involved in the care of patients that sometimes things get lost in the mix. Oftentimes it seems that there's not a single point person who's running the show. There are a lot of people coming in, different shifts and all, and so you need to be on top of it and make sure that everything's OK.

I think being on the other side every so often makes you a better physician, because sometimes we forget what it's like to be a patient or a family member of someone having surgery. Most families are terrified, especially when we come in as the physician with a plan, talking about open heart surgery, and things they might not understand. Being on the other side makes you remember the human aspect of it. You have to put yourself in their shoes from time to time. So, when a doctor says they're going to come by and then they don't, or a surgeon is meeting a patient and their family just two seconds before an operation—that's not the way that I would want to be treated, so I try and make sure that I don't treat my patients that way.

I really don't like to meet my patients and families for the first time on the day of surgery, although sometimes in an emergency it may be unavoidable. But in general, that's not something that I feel comfortable with. You're taking somebody's life in your hands—you're operating on them—and every operation, no matter how often you've done it, carries a risk. For the babies and infants, establishing a relationship with the parents is very important. Sometimes I've met the family in my office, so I've at least established a relationship with them even if I'm stuck in the OR during their scheduled pre-operative visit. I don't mind getting consent the morning of surgery if I've already met them. But unless it's an emergency or situation where a baby born that day needs surgery, I try to make sure I meet everyone ahead of time.

Education doesn't simply mean acquiring more cardiac knowledge, at least as far as Dr. G is concerned. Her continuing curiosity, medical and otherwise, leads to an almost constant desire to acquire new knowledge, even outside of surgery, medicine and the hospital.

Part of my life philosophy is to travel somewhere new—both inside and outside the United States—every year. Continue to learn about the world. Continue to ask questions. Never be bored. Boredom is my biggest fear in life. I figure the day I'm done learning is the day I'm buried. So, I try to learn something new every day. Even at night, I'll just jump on the computer and look through the news and see if there is something I can learn. Yesterday I was sitting in my own doctor's office, perusing a National Geographic travel book. I read about the Andaman Islands, and I wasn't sure where they were, so I said, "OK, that's my homework for tonight."

Leading others with less experience, to help them understand the difficulties and subtleties of medicine, is a major part of Dr. G's job.

The way that I lead my junior residents and my medical students is very different. My job is to be a good role model for the next generation of surgeons who want to be good pediatric cardiothoracic surgeons, or just surgeons in general. Just do your job and remember and remember the great quote: "Those who mind don't matter, and those who matter don't mind."

The students and residents are going to listen to me because we have a hierarchical arrangement where the chief of the service is over the senior faculty, who are over the junior faculty, who are over the fellows, who are over the residents, who are over the interns, who are over the medical students. That's the pecking order. In some ways, it's like the CEO of a company, the vice presidents and all that. I think it's very easy to be able to lead those who are below you in the natural pecking order. What's harder for you is to effectively lead up. And the big question always is, "How do you lead your leaders?"

I love teaching, and one of the things I love teaching is cardiac anatomy and physiology. Dr. Amy Juraszek is a cardiologist and cardiac morphologist here at Children's, and she and I are on a committee that certifies cardiac terminology for the International Society for Nomenclature of Paediatric and Congenital Heart Disease. We were at our first meeting in New York and this was right up my alley. You should have seen us, sitting in a conference room in the School of Medicine at Mount Sinai Hospital, discussing ventricular septal defects for five hours. Whether to call this one "conoventricular," "paramembranous," "perimembranous," or "cono septal." Lots of people on the committee drive each other crazy.

Dr. G's path toward pediatric heart surgery was not a traditional one, and thus required a slight detour or two.

The way I did it was general surgery, research, then the CT surgery fellowship, and from there, after nine years of study, I finally got to complete my congenital training. It wasn't written in stone, but back then you couldn't enter a cardiothoracic surgical residency without having completed a general surgical residency. Today, there are some combined programs called "Four-Three" programs—four years of general surgery, three years of cardiothoracic surgery, all in the same program. And the newest, I-6 integrated cardiothoracic surgical residency program. The point of these new programs is to integrate more relevant training in a shorter period of time.

One thing she learned early on that continues with Dr. G to this day is her sense of personal style.

I would always dress up for work when I was doing my general surgical training. I would dress up during my residency and fellowship days, too. I remember being in the trauma room when I was in surgical training and a penetrating chest wound came in. I wound up with blood all over my clothes. When I took them to the dry cleaner, he looked at me very suspiciously.

CASE NOTES PATIENT: CPR FLORES DOB: 4/18/2013

CPR Flores lucked out. His cardiac abnormality would bring him to Dr. Guleserian for the heart surgery she calls her favorite, an arterial switch operation. "CPR" isn't his real first name, by the way, but we'll get to that in a bit.

CPR was born in Amarillo, Texas on April 18, 2013, and he was in trouble from the start. He had "d-transposition of the great arteries," his aorta and pulmonary artery were switched. The deoxygenated blood fed immediately back into the aorta, so oxygen-poor blood was perpetually circulating through his body. The only things that keep a transposition patient alive are the atrial septal defect and the ductus arteriosus, which remain open after birth allowing some red blood to mix with the copious blue blood. Except in the case of CPR Flores. His atrial septum was nearly intact, which actually worked against him. Doctors in Amarillo intubated him so he could get enough oxygen to survive. He was transferred to Children's by medical jet, and when he arrived he looked, as they say around the hospital, blue as a squid.

CPR Flores seemed determined to stay on the tough road. Upon arrival at the hospital he went into cardiac arrest, and doctors performed cardiopulmonary resuscitation for 32 minutes to keep him alive.

The big question when he came in was, "Do we even bother to do anything here?" There was a lot of discussion very quickly about whether this little guy could even withstand a balloon atrial septostomy (a bedside procedure where a catheter is fed through the groin into the heart, to insert a balloon in the septum to keep it open). *The decision was made to go for it, and see if we could help him.*

Time became critical. Nurse practitioner Kimberly Moore asked Dr. G when she was going to get Flores into surgery.

"Which Flores?" Dr. G asked her, since there were two baby boys on the unit with the same last name.

"CPR Flores," Moore replied, creating the nickname by which he would be known around the Heart Center from then on.

The procedure he needed is called an arterial switch operation, where we transect the aorta and pulmonary artery so that we can switch them. Sounds simple, but we also need to transfer the tiny, 1-mm coronary arteries from what was the old pulmonary artery to the neoaorta. This is my favorite operation to perform because of the technical intricacy necessary to transfer the tiny coronary arteries, and also because it restores the heart's anatomy to what was intended. This means a normal life for CPR Flores, no ongoing medication, no restrictions on what he can do. The best time for me to perform this surgery is about day five of the infant's life. He was scheduled to have his surgery on April 26th. I called the ICU to ask if everything was OK and see if he was he ready for surgery, and they said, "Yes, he's ready to go." But of course, I always have to go check everything myself. I looked through all the labs, the imaging studies and I saw that his last head ultrasound showed increasing cerebral edema (brain swelling).

I said we needed to get another ultrasound and they told me he was already in the OR, so I said let's get one in there. This ultrasound showed that the edema was better, but now there was a new bleed in his head. So, it was back to ICU, no surgery. During open-heart surgery, we have to give heparin, a blood thinner, so blood won't clot in the heart-lung bypass machine. The blood thinner could turn a small bleed into a big bleed, which leads to increased chances of brain damage, and even death. I could do a perfect operation, yet wind up with a brain-dead patient. So, I wanted to wait.

It's not like I don't trust anybody, but sometimes I don't trust anybody. In my mind, bad data is worse than no data. The stakes are way too high for inaccurate information. So, we consulted with our neurological colleagues and asked when it would be safe, from a neurologic standpoint, to perform the operation. They said two weeks out would be fine, so his surgery was set for May 6th. We did the switch; he had an uneventful recovery. He was discharged and went home a week later. He did great.

So great that on his first birthday, his family called the hospital and asked if they could come in and throw a little party for everybody to celebrate. And more recently Samuel Flores turned three. His mother, Kimberly, says he's doing very well.

"Dr. G is a miracle worker," Kimberly says. "We just appreciate everything she did for him so much. From the way she handled the surgery, to the way she gave us all the information we needed before. She's amazing."

CHAPTER TEN

Procurement—Going After the Heart

"The closer, the better."

Transplant surgeons deal with a life-and-death component in their work every day. Because it's such a fundamental part of the job, it's often expressed in a very blunt manner. The ethical dilemma of the transplant is a constant presence in the OR: one person must die for another person to live. The words that follow may seem cold in their frankness, but that's only because you're reading them in the abstract. Dr. Guleserian and her colleagues feel the ethical, moral, and personal nature of their work in the extreme. The verbal shorthand they employ, the jargon, is a part of their world and no disrespect is ever even implied, let alone intended.

In terms of identifying potential donors for any type of organ transplantation the donor first has to be declared brain dead. Once the declaration of brain death has been made, an organ procurement organization (OPO) *is contacted to approach the family. If the patient has consented in advance, then everything is set. Some families, for whatever reason, will refuse. Not everybody agrees.*

Donor information is sent out to transplant centers around the country, based on medical urgency, geographic location, and information specific to recipients. When I look at the donor offer, I look at the manner of death. In a motor vehicle accident, for instance, there may be head trauma, where the cause of death is intracranial hemorrhage. You hope all the rest of the organs are okay. But with blunt trauma from a motor vehicle accident there could also be other internal organ injuries—lung contusion, cardiac contusion, liver laceration, splenic laceration. A series of imaging studies is performed—chest X-rays, CT-scans, brain scans, echocardiograms—to check for injuries that can't be observed, and then lab tests are run to determine the functional capacity of the organs as well as what they look like externally. So, if it's an isolated head injury, like a ruptured cerebral aneurysm or a gunshot wound to the head, typically the rest of the organs are okay as long as there hasn't been a significant amount of time without oxygen being delivered throughout the body. Every detail will be made known to us by the OPO. Ideally, you want to preserve every organ that you can to the best of your ability, and that's what OPO's like the Southwest Transplant Alliance, who we work with at Children's, do so well.

Thousands of patients across the country are on donor lists waiting for different organs to become available. But the level of complexity increases when you realize there is more to a match than just matching a patient with the organ they require.

For purposes of this discussion, let's assume that the donor heart, lungs, liver, intestines, pancreas, and kidneys are all good. Say I have twelve patients on my recipient list and the donor is a three-year old who weighs fifteen kilograms. I see three or four patients on my list this donor could be good for. On our end, many things go into consideration for the recipient. There's blood type, donor's size, quality of the donor organ, and a number of other criteria. For example, if the recipient has specific antibodies, then the match may not be good. We have to look very carefully for all that. We assess every donor-recipient match in extraordinary detail.

Everything up to this point has been preliminary. Once the donor heart is accepted, an intricate dance begins—the timing of different surgical teams in different cities, all working toward one end.

We call our recipient family if they're not already in the hospital. If they're here, they are either in the CVICU, in the step-down unit, or in the ward on C8. We have labs done. Blood products are made available for the procedure. Immunosuppressive medication is begun. Consent for the procedure has to be obtained. All sorts of things. At the same time, preparations for the donor procurement are underway. Our transplant coordinators will be calling the organ procurement team at the donor hospital, which could be here at Children's, in a nearby hospital, or several states away.

We continue to assess and reassess that the donor quality is good, that there's been no deterioration in heart or other organ function, and then we start making plans to get our procurement team to the donor site. Say we're taking the heart here in Dallas, the St. Louis team is taking the lungs, the intestines are going to the Houston team, the liver and pancreas are going to Arkansas, and someone in New Orleans is going to take the kidneys. All the different teams have to coordinate. We start looking at things like distances, what the flying time will be, what the weather conditions are, what the driving time will be on both ends, from airport to hospital and vice versa, the need for a helicopter in rush hour traffic. We take that all into consideration, and once that timeline is known, then we start making preparations for the recipient to get to the OR.

Our procurement team heads to the donor hospital, and they bring a cooler filled with ice and with cardioplegia solution, the chemical solution we use to stop and preserve the donor heart. We bring all our own equipment with us, just in case we get to the donor site and there is something lacking there. One of our cardiothoracic surgeons, usually one of my partners, goes on a procurement, along with one of our fellows or a surgical technician. We sometimes have students who want to go along to observe. We fly out of Love field on a private jet. Once we land at the recipient city there is medical transport to the donor hospital. The OPO from the other centers will be there. It might be Mid-America Transplant from St. Louis or LifeGift from Houston. We'll meet with their representatives. And one of the Southwest Transplant Alliance representatives comes with us.

If I go to the donor site, the first thing I do when I go into the OR is to find the scrub tech and introduce myself. When I've got an abdominal team standing between me and the scrub tech, I need to know who's handing me instruments. The very first thing I do is make a point of learning the scrub tech's name. Believe me, that's key. Once you make that introduction and treat them well, they'll be treating you well in return.

The donor is brought into the operating room, already intubated with lines in place, because they've been kept on life support to keep the organs alive. We verify that this is the donor, that the blood type is correct, and that the match for the donor and recipient is accurate. Then the donor is prepped and draped.

At this point, the communication between the different teams is important because when we clamp the heart and deliver cardioplegia we want to be sure that they're ready when we're ready. Once we stop the heart, that's it. We're not on bypass here, so all the organ preservation needs to happen simultaneously, and we coordinate that. Once we're ready, we verify with the OR team back home that it's OK to cross-clamp, and then we clamp the aorta, deliver the cardioplegia, take ice and place it into the chest cavity as we're emptying blood from the heart. Once the heart is stopped and the full amount of cardioplegia has been delivered, we remove the heart with whatever extra vessels and things we might need for reconstruction. We place the heart into a sterile container filled with cardioplegia solution, and pack that container in ice in three sterile plastic bags. We put the heart container into the cooler along with several donor lymph nodes and samples of blood so we can do a retrospective cross-match, to be sure that there are no unsuitable antibody-antigen.

The first organ removed is the heart, then the lungs, and then the abdominal organs. The reason for that order is that for heart and lung transplantation you want to get them in to the recipient within four to six hours, in general a heart within four, lungs within six to eight. The liver and the kidneys can go longer than that. In some instances, kidneys can go for up to twenty-four hours. But it's always best to keep the ischemic time as short as possible.

From this moment on, transplantation is mainly about transportation. Transportation involves time, and time is critical when your carry-on baggage contains a human heart.

When we're done at the donor hospital, we get back into the ambulance that will take us back to the airport—lights and siren full-on—we'll board our aircraft and take off. And again, each step of the way we're letting our colleagues back in the OR know that we're en route and what the clamp time was. Once we land at Dallas Love Field, Children's Medical Center ambulance gets us back to the hospital—lights and sirens again full on.

Of course, nothing is guaranteed. There have been occasions when, despite everybody's best efforts, things don't work out at the procurement site, and families will suffer disappointment.

One time we arrived at the donor center and as they were bringing the donor from the ICU to the operating room the donor went into cardiac arrest and they started doing CPR in the elevator. We had just traveled two and a half hours to get to Tucson, Arizona—but that was it. We had to leave. And that's a bad situation for everybody. Another time we had an older donor in his twenties or thirties. The donor had no history of risk factors, nothing to warrant a cardiac catheterization at any time. For donors over forty, or anyone with risk factors for heart disease, a cardiac cath is usually done first to look for coronary artery disease. But this twenty-seven-year old didn't have any history. When that donor heart got back to our OR, I noticed there was coronary artery disease. It's rare, but it can happen.

The thought that life and death are hanging over every operation is an ever-present one. The top surgeons understand the risks, and know how to learn from every experience.

There are different situations that occur not only with transplants but any type of surgery. There are different reasons why some patients don't survive. You might be performing what's considered an easy operation, but on a very sick patient with multiple risk factors. You could do a very high risk, complex operation on a patient who is relatively healthy. Or, you might have the worst-case scenario, a high-risk, complex operation on a patient with what we call 'poor protoplasm.' For example, a patient with chromosomal abnormality, brain injury, prematurity, low-birth-weight, and/or multiple organ system abnormalities who needs an operation. The risk profile is just tremendous.

It's very, very rare for a patient to die in the operating room. I've seen it happen—not to me yet, but you never know if there will be a day. There are going to be patients who die due to circumstances beyond your control, meaning that they come in and the diagnosis is made late, or they're hemodynamically unstable when heading to the OR and you're just trying your best to do what you can do. When you don't get the outcome you anticipated, you always need to figure out why. It's usually never an individual that's responsible for a bad outcome, though it can be. If you're sure that everything was fine operatively, and all your post-op imaging studies and hemodynamic measures indicate that everything went well, then you have to look at systems. Was there some sort of system failure? Communication failure, equipment failure, medication error, break in the usual system? Or, did nobody recognize that the child was sicker than they thought?

The good ones take it personally.

CHAPTER ELEVEN

Transplant

"What we do here is a team sport."

After the Southwest Transplant Alliance put in more than a full day of work on one particular donor, they listed organs from that donor as being available for transplant. The page Dr. G never thought she'd get finally came on October 5, 2011.

I got the page that there was a donor heart available for Rylynn. I jumped right on to the DonorNet website and saw where the donor was located, that the weight and blood type were appropriate, and that the donor quality was perfect. I reviewed the echo, all the lab tests, and medications that the donor was being supported on. I took a quick look at the antigen profile—there were lots listed and I was concerned that this match might not work because Rylynn was highly sensitized and there was a long list of donor antigens that I would need to confirm would be OK for her. I'm always cautious. (It's not that I don't trust anybody, but remember when Adam Vinatieri kicked the field goal for the Patriots' first Super Bowl win? I was watching the game on TV and then, just to make certain I wasn't imagining things, I called my dad to make sure I'd seen it right.)

I called Susan Daneman, our transplant coordinator, and told her to take a look and get the ball rolling. Somehow she already knew that this donor was a perfect match for Ry. The transplant cardiology and immunology teams confirmed the news. The match was our biggest hurdle. After that there was there was a laundry list of things that needed to be done. We had to let the family know, we had to get pre-operative blood work, we had to make the patient NPO (no food allowed), *lots of things. The entire surgical team needed to be notified—the anesthesiology team, our scrub techs, nurses, respiratory therapists, perfusion team, CVICU team, Child Life, Social Work. And because she was part of our reality TV series, we had to notify the local ABC affiliate that produced the show so they could be there to film. Also, one of the things about this case that made it more difficult was that Rylynn was being supported by a Berlin Heart, so I needed our VAD coordinator in the OR with us to trouble-shoot anything that might happen before, and while, we disconnected the VAD and got her on bypass.*

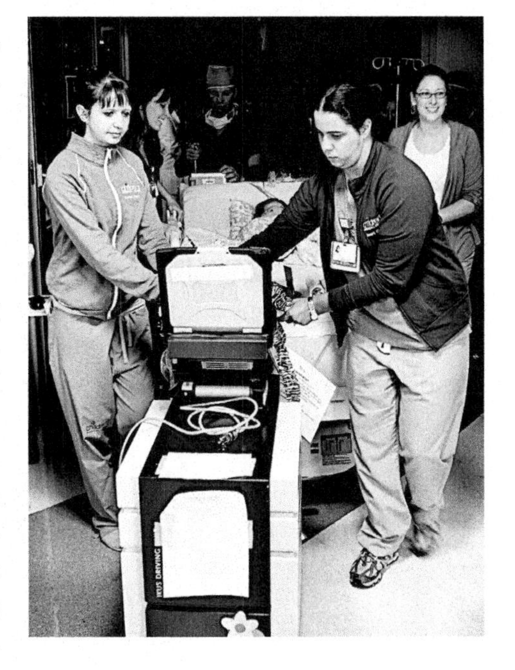

Early in the morning on October 6th Rylynn was wheeled out of her CVICU room. The procession to the second-floor OR was slow and precise. The large Berlin Heart pump had to be rolled carefully in front of the bed. It was a tight squeeze just getting everything into the hallway.

As the caravan approached the elevators, everything stopped, and Andrea and Gilly said goodbye to their daughter in another hospital hallway.

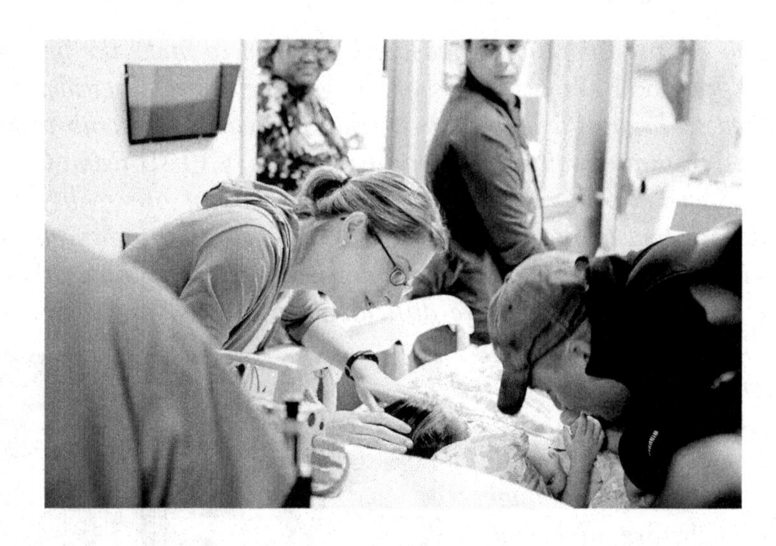

It was 2:27 AM.

Rylynn had a doll clutched tightly in her arms as her bed was wheeled into the operating room. She was only two years old, but she was calm and quiet as she looked at all the masked grownups standing over her. A nurse said to Rylynn, “If you let me have your doll, we’ll take good care of her until you’re back in your room.”

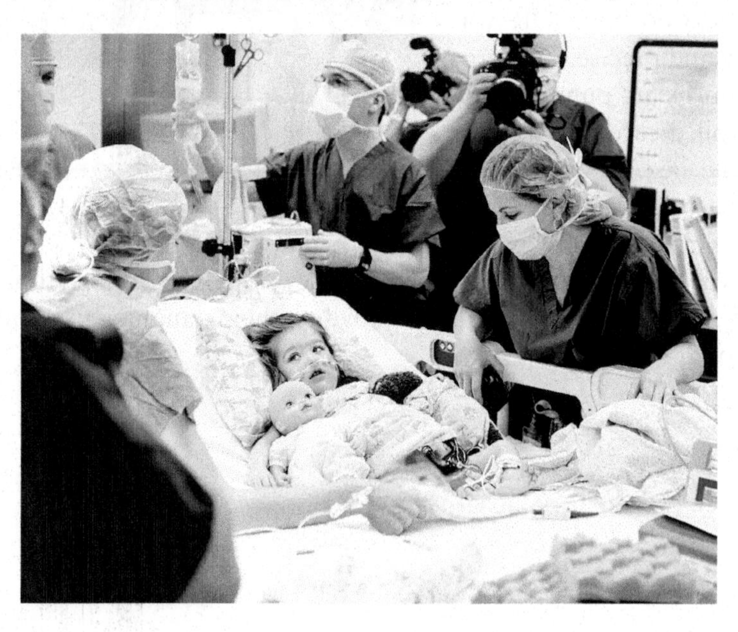

Rylynn calmly surrendered her doll. She was transferred from her CVICU bed to the operating table, and the anesthesiologists began the process of putting her under. Rylynn was the only one who would sleep. Neither the surgical team nor Rylynn's family had slept since word of a donor heart came in yesterday afternoon, and nobody would sleep until after the transplant was finished.

I went into the OR with the team wheeling Rylynn in. The time before scrubbing in is kind of our pregame pep talk. We go over our game plan in detail, the specifics about the surgical plan, perfusion strategy, special equipment, even prepping and draping. For example, I may want her neck exposed in case I have to crash on bypass (get on bypass faster than usual to deal with an emergency of some sort.) *Before we do anything at all, we confirm the patient's name and medical record number, blood type, weight, date of birth, diagnosis, and planned operation. We review allergies, anticipated blood loss, the surgical site to be operated on, immunosuppression ordered, antibiotics administered, and make sure we have sufficient blood products in the OR. And, at all times, we're in communication with the donor procurement team constantly checking their travel and estimated arrival time.*

In addition to the medical team, the family team was mobilizing. The part of the Riojas family not already in Dallas when the news came—grandparents, aunts, uncles—was soon on the road, headed to Children's from various parts of Texas. (At 10:00 PM Dr. G mobilized me. The text read, "Transplanting Rylynn. Start about 3:00 AM." I couldn't wait. I got dressed and headed for the hospital. I could sleep tomorrow.)

Dr. Mahesh Sharma, Dr. G's junior partner, led the procurement team. The flight was just under 40 minutes each way, which meant the cold ischemic time would most certainly be under the desired four hours.

Rylynn was anesthetized. An arterial line was placed into the radial artery in her left wrist to monitor blood pressure and draw blood gases. A central venous line was inserted into her right internal jugular vein to monitor central venous pressure and to administer medications during the procedure. The Broviac catheter already in place would be used for additional access. Her PD catheter would act as a passive drain for the heart failure-caused fluid that continued to accumulate in her abdomen. Rylynn was given immunosuppressive medications to prevent rejection of the donor heart, the foreign organ about to be placed in her body. One of those medications is Basiliximab, a chimeric mouse-human monoclonal antibody. In other words, it's a drug derived from blood tumor cells in mice.

It was 3:02 AM.

Rylynn was a hospital celebrity because of the publicity surrounding her case and OR-6 was packed for her surgery. It was a cramped room under the best of conditions. The extra compliment of CVICU nurses watching over Rylynn's Berlin Heart, the entire surgical team, plus a videography team from the Children's Med TV show, and two still photographers filled the room. It was SRO. Dr. G and her assistant, Dr. Javier Brenes-Gonzales, her congenital heart surgery fellow, stepped up into the operative field.

It was 4:55 AM.

Susan Daneman was on the phone with the procurement team from the moment they departed Dallas for the donor hospital. The precisely timed schedule—operating time, ambulance time, and flying time—had to be adhered to. When she got the word from the procurement team that the donor heart had been visualized and was a go, Dr. G went to work.

Once all the various procurement teams were in the operating room with the donor, the heart team opened the chest to visualize the heart. It all looked good, so they gave us the go-ahead. At that point, we administered the immunosuppression medication, and started the re-do median sternotomy (re-opening the scar and re-dividing the sternum) *on Rylynn. I never make a chest incision until I know that the donor heart has been visualized and looks good. You just never know.*

There are many teams involved at the donor end. If they tell us they're going to cross-clamp the heart in 15 minutes, now I'm doing the math in my head. If you can cross-clamp in 15 minutes and it takes roughly ten minutes to get the heart out, that's 25 minutes, and it takes another ten minutes or so to get to the airport, that's 35 minutes, and it's a 40-minute flight, and ten minutes on the ground to Children's and five minutes to get to the OR, is that enough time for me to dissect through all the scar tissue?

There were dense adhesions from Rylynn's multiple previous surgical procedures, including her pulmonary artery stent placement and the Berlin Heart implantation. All the protective Gore-Tex wrapping and extensive scar tissue had to be carefully peeled away from the Berlin Heart, the chest wall, the lungs, and the diaphragm.

Everything was stuck to everything.

The remaining pericardium, the sac surrounding the heart, was stuck to the fragile, dilated right atrium. The phrenic nerve, which basically controls the diaphragm and breathing, goes down the neck between the heart and lungs. It was plastered to a previous suture line on the right atrium. The stent to enlarge her left pulmonary artery was visible through the vessel wall—it had grown into the back of the neo-aorta, the most dangerous place it could adhere to. In other words, there was a lot of very delicate work to do.

There are some things the echo, the cardiac catheterization, the CT angiogram, the MRI —whatever imaging studies you have—can't tell you about beforehand; for one, how extensive the adhesions might be. There are clues in the images about some structures in the area that may not be ideal. But you have no idea how difficult the chip out will be, how bad the scar tissue is. Some chip outs are quick, 15 minutes. Some can take up to two hours. It's like a Christmas present. You never know what you get until you open the box.

What the imaging did tell me was that Rylynn needed a pulmonary arterioplasty (repair of the pulmonary artery) *as well as an aortoplasty* (repair of the aorta). *The pulmonary artery stent had become part of the pulmonary arterial wall, so I couldn't remove it completely. I would have to filet it open and anastomose the donor pulmonary arterial tree to her pulmonary artery and its branches. Because she'd had a Damus-Kaye-Stansel aortopulmonary anastomosis* (her pulmonary artery was joined to her aorta at the time of the Norwood procedure, her first surgery), *her aorta was foreshortened, much wider and more delicate than a normal aorta. And because the stent had eroded into a thinned-out area of her aorta, we had to do a little bit of an aortic reconstruction as well.*

"A little bit of an aortic reconstruction" meant quickly getting onto cardiopulmonary bypass, disconnecting Rylynn from the Berlin Heart, cooling her body temperature down to 64.4 degrees Fahrenheit, packing her head in ice to protect her brain, and inducing circulatory arrest. Her blood was then drained out of her body into the pump, leaving her, for the moment, with no circulation to her body or brain. This gave Dr. G a few minutes to operate in a bloodless field, the best way to do what was needed to repair Rylynn's aorta. In order to aid in the cooling, the temperature in the OR is turned down to 65 degrees. Those who aren't directly working at a given moment try to keep warm.

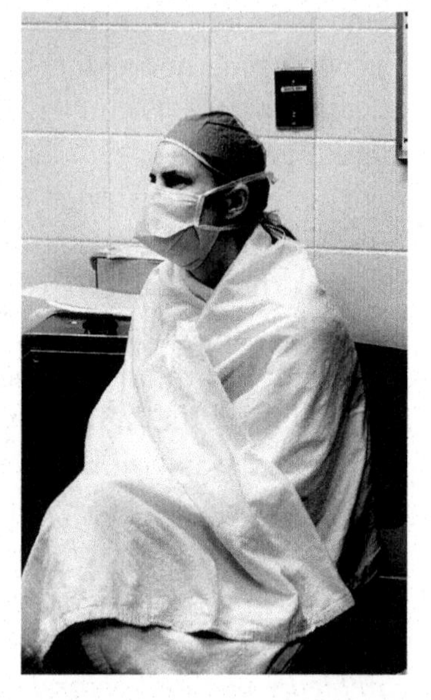

This wasn't a slam-dunk transplant. It already took longer than usual to get in there. I had to go on pump earlier than planned and stop Rylynn's circulation to fix the hole in her aorta where the stent had eroded. She had lots of aortopulmonary collaterals. She was profoundly cyanotic, and cyanotic kids tend to have increased bleeding in general, plus she'd been on blood-thinners and anti-platelet agents to prevent clotting with the Berlin Heart. Getting her bleeding under control was a little trickier than usual because of all that. Frankly, it was a bloody mess.

We just used circulatory arrest for a short period of time. With her aorta repaired, while she was on bypass, we did the rest of the dissection. Once you're safely on pump you have the luxury of the heart being decompressed, and you can dissect out the atria, ventricles and vessels more easily and safely. Otherwise with a dilated, poorly functioning heart there can be a lot of irritability when you use the Bovie. The heart can fibrillate, or just stop—complete cardiac arrest. Once your patient is safely on bypass you—well, I—could breathe a bit.

It was 7:30 AM.

Time is relative in the OR. There's a clock on the wall, but with no windows to let in light there is no external indication of time of day. As the hours go by and the clock says 3:45 you have to stop and figure out whether that's AM or PM. Your circadian rhythm has been short-circuited. The drama that takes place in the center of the room expands and contracts time as well. An intense period of activity seems to fly by, yet by that OR clock it took fifty-five minutes.

Time was dragging in a third-floor waiting room. Andrea had complained in her blog about all the nursing she'd been forced to learn during Rylynn's extended ICU stay—she just wanted to be Mommy. Once she and Gilly kissed Rylynn goodbye in the hallway hours before she was nothing but Mommy, and now she knew it.

"There's a lot of fear and anxiety in it, because you hear stories about things that can go wrong during the surgery, or something with the donor," Andrea said. "So up until about 6:00 AM, when they told us the transplant was actually beginning, up to then it was just complete fear. You just sit, and wait for each of those updates from the nurses about what's happening, and at each critical stage they try to tell you what's going on, but there's not much you can do."

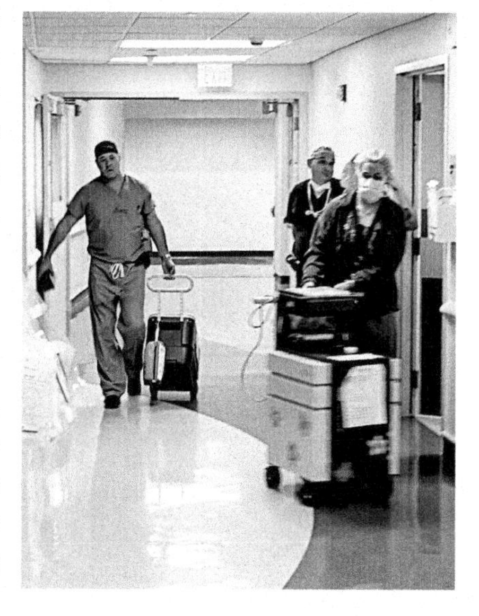

* * *

Medicine, technology, and human drama met in a momentary confluence in the hallway outside OR-6. The Berlin Heart—the pump that extended Rylynn's life for months while she waited for a donor heart—had been disconnected and was wheeled out of the OR at the exact moment that the cooler containing her new heart was wheeled in. It couldn't have been staged any better in a TV hospital drama.

It was 8:57 AM.

The final steps in removing Rylynn's original heart began.

I wait until the donor heart is in the hospital because although it's extremely rare, something can go wrong—a problem with the donor, weather problems, an accident along the way, anything unexpected. I like to stay on the safe side. There have been times when there was information we didn't know about. One time, they mixed up the donor weight and told us the donor was 86 pounds. When the procurement team got there, they found the donor really weighed 86 kilos—190 pounds—so the heart was way too big.

Dr. G cut the tubing connecting the Berlin Heart to Rylynn's ventricle. She removed the remnants of the pump, and then lifted out the heart that had struggled to keep Rylynn alive. That failed heart was now in plain view on a side table in the OR. It looked like a large hamburger steak that had been pounded flat. A wide piece of plastic from the Berlin Heart stuck out of the ventricle.

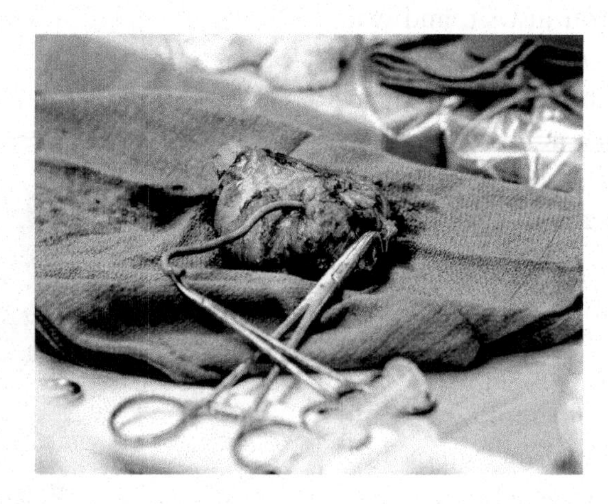

It was 9:11 AM.

Remember, she had an abnormal heart to begin with: hypoplastic left heart syndrome. She didn't have a left ventricle to speak of. She had a very diseased heart, so it was dilated; parts were hypertrophied—thickened. And then, when you take the heart out there's no blood in it, so it's deflated like a balloon with no air left in it.

Like all transplant recipients, Rylynn's course wasn't an easy one.

Being on the cardiopulmonary bypass circuit can induce a systemic inflammatory response and that's not good for the lungs, especially if the bypass time is prolonged. The good thing is that our perfusionists at Children's—in this particular case, Ron Gorney—take off that extra volume using a technique called ultrafiltration. What you can't change are leaky capillaries. Sometimes you're already behind the eight ball. Kids in florid heart failure often feel so sick they don't want to eat; their nutrition is so poor that their protein levels are low and they have anasarca (total body swelling)*—they look like a mini-Michelin man.*

Rylynn was a single ventricle patient on a ventricular assist device, with a PD catheter in place that was draining fluid from her belly continuously. She was losing protein from there and wasn't eating much. She was still cyanotic, very volume overloaded, and had lungs that weren't perfect. And now we're adding a pump insult to all of that.

The blue and white cooler that was wheeled into the OR might well have been full of beer for a fishing trip. Except for the large label on the top reading HUMAN ORGAN/TISSUE FOR TRANSPLANT. Scrub tech Dave Bartoo, who had gone with the heart procurement team, was now scrubbed in. He opened the cooler and removed the ice, then lifted out the triple-bagged plastic jar. When the heart was removed from the jar, he handed it to Dr. G. It looked like an uncooked chicken breast.

The sequence of events in the OR now picked up speed, because the most difficult part was over.

Before we were ready to start the actual transplant procedure, the donor pericardium was used to complete the hilum-to-hilum pulmonary artery reconstruction (the connection between the pulmonary artery branches and the lungs). *The new heart was carefully brought up into the operative field, wrapped in an icy gauze pad. The first anastomosis completed was the left atrium, then the inferior vena cava, then the pulmonary arteries, and then the aorta. There was a pretty good size discrepancy between the donor and recipient aorta* (the recipient aorta was larger than the donor) *so a tapering aortoplasty was necessary.*

In just under an hour Dr. G was able to reconstruct the pulmonary artery and complete four of the five new connections. She then de-aired the heart and took the cross clamp off, restoring blood flow to a heart that had been lifeless for over 3 hours.

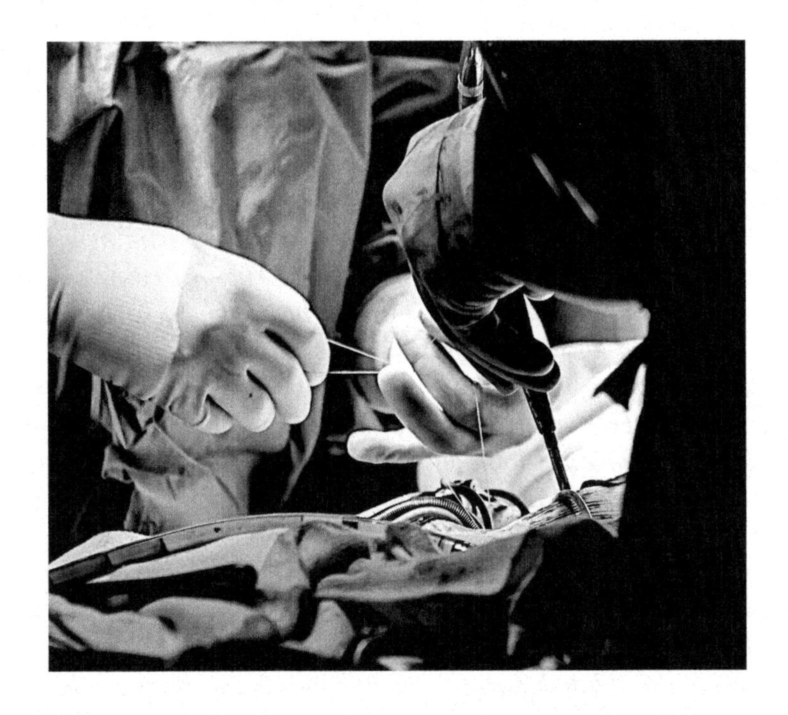

At that point, the table is tilted so the patient's head is down. We start nitroglycerin and then the anesthesiologist starts puffing on the lungs to get all the air out of the heart, so it doesn't embolize and go to the brain or other parts of the body. Then we release the aortic cross-clamp. The blood flows into the coronary arteries and washes out the cardioplegia solution we used to stop the heart when it was taken from the donor. The heart begins to beat again. First one beat. Then two. Then, pretty soon it gets back to normal sinus rhythm.

The magic moment came. A heart that had been beating in somebody else's body only hours earlier was vigorously powering Rylynn's blood throughout her system. The beep-beep-beep on the vital signs monitor returned to mark the new heart rhythm. Pacing wires placed onto the heart would be left sticking out through the skin and connected to a temporary pacemaker, to correct any rhythm abnormality in the first few CVICU days.

It was 11:10 AM.

We complete the superior vena cava anastomosis while the heart is beating. Once that's done, we release the caval tapes that we put around the vena cavae at the start of the operation. That allows the blue blood to return to the right side of the heart and continue through the right heart—back to normal circulation. We keep re-warming, start IV medications to support the new heart and then are ready to do the post-op echo. The procedure is done, and we have a normal four-chambered heart now. The new heart is working, and it's like any other successful heart operation at this point. I know it sounds like I'm downplaying this, but it's routine at this point. (Everybody has his or her own skill set, right? When I walk on a plane and I look left into the cockpit, I see all that stuff and I think, "I could never fly this plane." I can't even drive a stick shift. I grew up in the city. I live in the city. There's no reason to drive a stick shift. Besides, if you drive a stick, how can you text? Just kidding!)

The big challenge with this heart transplant was dealing with the stent, the dilated aorta, and Rylynn's lung disease. She was also on anticoagulants because of the Berlin Heart, so she bled more than normal. She also had aorta pulmonary collaterals (extra blood vessels branching off the aorta going to the arteries going to the lungs) *because her left pulmonary artery was very small, which means there was increased blood return to the heart, which meant there was more blood flooding my operative field than normal during the procedure. All that plus the fact she was on three different anticoagulants and antiplatelet agents, coupled with her chronic liver dysfunction—let's just say her intrinsic ability to clot was very impaired. She bled like stink. So, yes—it was a struggle. She was definitely one of our highest-risk transplants. But she was rocking it.*

Dr. Poonam Thankavel performed the trans-esophageal echocardiogram for a look at how things were functioning. The lights in the OR were turned a dark lime green, to make it easier for surgeons to visualize the echo monitor. Every head in the OR was turned to the screen.

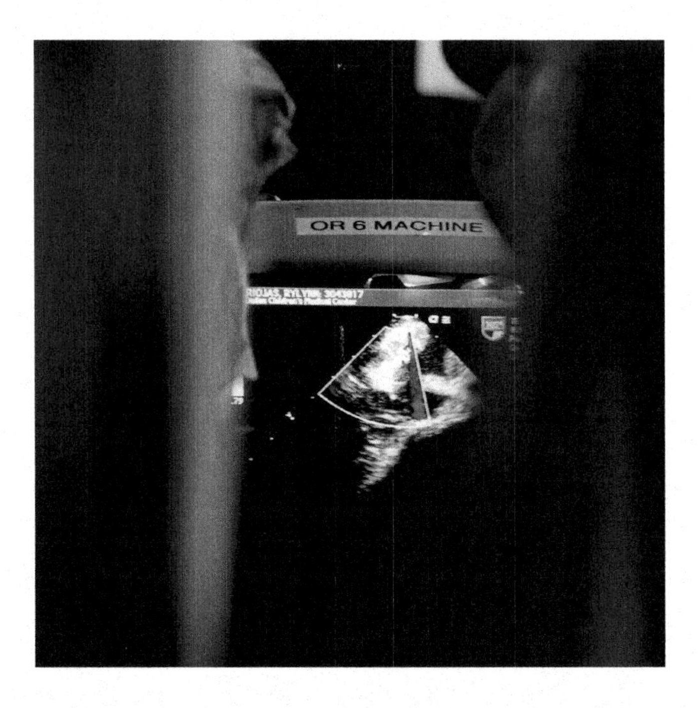

The surgeons and cardiologists were pleased. The echo showed only trivial amounts of regurgitation in the mitral valve and mild regurgitation in the tricuspid valve. Blood flow was unimpeded and pressures through various parts of the heart were as desired.

Now all we had left was to place some drains and close her chest and close the exit sites where her Berlin Heart cannulae had been.

Rylynn received multiple units of packed red blood cells, platelets, cryoprecipitate, and fresh frozen plasma—all to help the clotting process.

And one more stat: While most of the team had changed shifts on and off during the transplant surgery, Dr. G and Dr. Brenes-Gonzales were in the game the entire time. Dr. G climbed on to her step stool at 4:55 AM. She stepped down at 2:25 PM. No pauses, no breaks, no food, no water. Just surgery.

Rylynn was transferred to her CVICU bed in the OR, next to the doll the OR nurses placed there before surgery began.

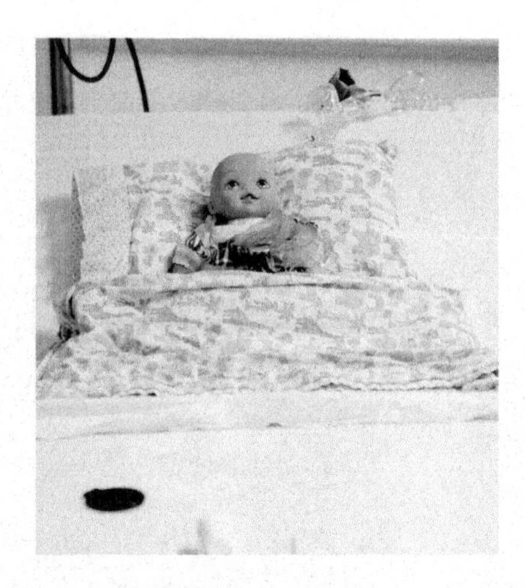

Dr. G accompanied the OR team from the second floor to the CVICU on three. The procession stopped in the third-floor hallway for a "drive-by" greeting from Andrea and Gilly. The reunion was an emotional one, even though Rylynn was unconscious. Andrea noted Rylynn's changed skin color, no blue showing anywhere. Her lips were finally pink.

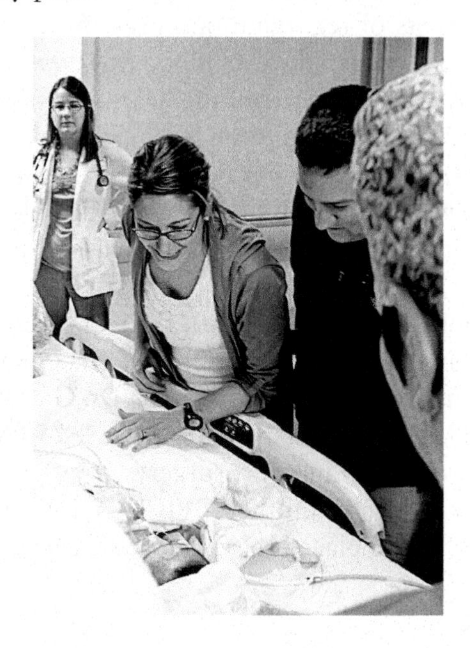

The team continued down the hall to Rylynn's CVICU room. Lots of prep had been done awaiting her arrival. The handoff from the surgeons and anesthesiologists to the CVICU team is a delicate moment for Dr. G.

When you come off pump you have a nicely functioning heart, things should be fine. Technically, the heart you have now is better than what you had before. But these patients will almost always have right ventricular dysfunction within the first 24 hours. The tricuspid valve might not have been leaking at all, but now you have some because the valve has dilated during the first night. Plus, when you're giving blood products, when you're resuscitating the patient, you're adding more volume to the heart. It may be a bit dilated on its own, and then you're adding volume, and it dilates more, and is often pumping against higher resistance in the lungs. You can get into some pretty bad right heart failure if it's not managed appropriately. There are drugs to administer. Rylynn was on epinephrine, milrinone, nitroglycerin, inhaled nitric oxide, IV fluids, antibiotics, sedation medications plus her immunosuppressive medications. Lots to manage. Caring for the patient post-transplant is very challenging. That's why what we do here is a team sport.

Remember that going into this her nutrition wasn't great (not any fault of her parents—she just felt so terrible she wasn't eating). *Her albumin, or protein level, was very low and the pressure in her veins was high because of the failing Glenn physiology, even though she had the Berlin Heart. When you have low protein levels and high venous pressures, fluid leaks from the inside the blood vessels to the surrounding tissues, and you get edema or anasarca, the total body swelling we saw so much of with Rylynn. So, there were more than the usual obstacles in her post-surgical care.*

Dr. G left the CVICU and headed for one of the most rewarding parts of the procedure. Walking quickly as usual, even after ten straight hours on her feet at the operating table, Dr. G led Susan Daneman around a corner, through a double door where Andrea and Gilly sat waiting in a small family conference room. There were hugs all around.

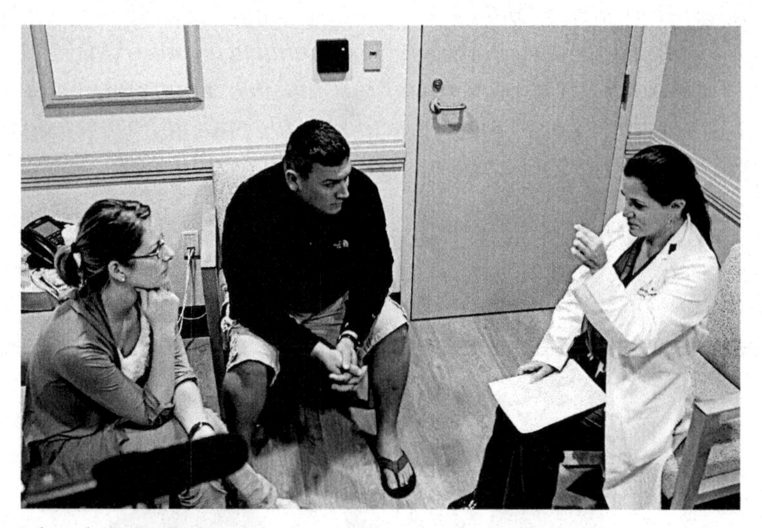

(photo by Lou Curtis)

The parents sat quietly, hunched forward in their chairs as Dr. G told them the new heart was fantastic, very strong, beating well. The EKG was excellent. She talked about some of the obstacles that came up, especially the problem freeing the aorta from the stented pulmonary artery. And then with a laugh she told the parents that

Rylynn's heart finally had two ventricles and the normal four chambers. Andrea laughed, too.

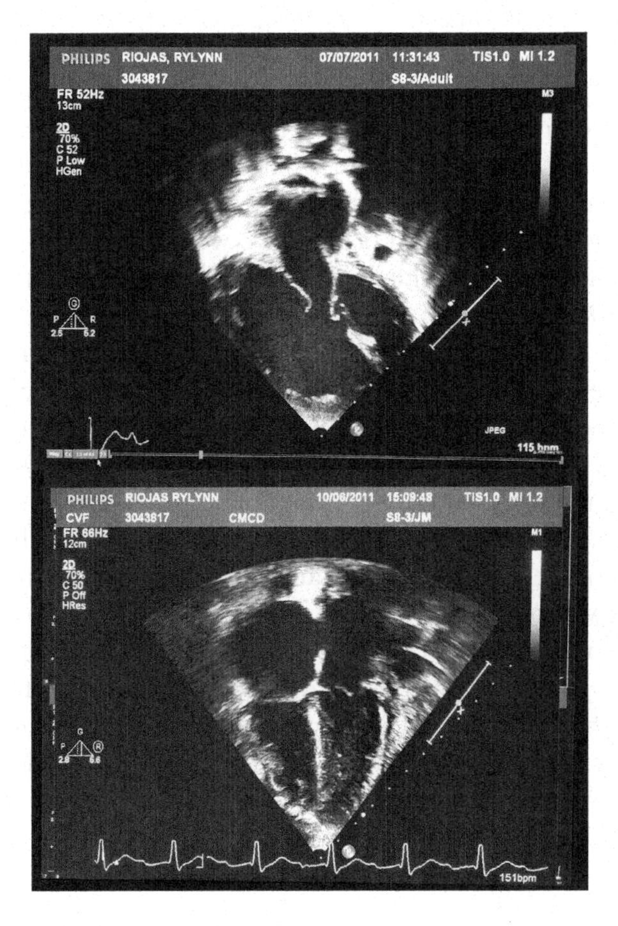

"The second time we got to go into her CVICU room after the transplant," Andrea said, "the technician had just finished an echo of her new heart, and he was kind enough to show us a few images. The first one came up, and it had four chambers in it, and I was just kind of surprised. I really don't know why it shocked me the way it did but it did, to see it like that. It was wonderful."

Andrea's hospital experience with Rylynn would have a profound effect on her professional life. Andrea's months in the CVICU would help her to go back to her architect's drawing board and design healthcare facilities from a new perspective.

"Now, I think through every design as if I were the patient, the parents of the patient, or the family of the patient. I obviously tried to do this from the beginning of my career, but now it's personal! I can actually imagine what it's like day-in and day-out in a patient room. I know what works and what doesn't. We've spent time in nearly every department of a hospital, so I feel like I have a little to add to each situation. And because we were inpatient for so long, I feel like I got a real inside look at the physician and nursing staff point of view as well."

Dr. G returned to Rylynn's CVICU room and began to wind down. She leaned back against a counter, took out her phone and before she checked her messages, she looked up at me and let out a huge sigh. Even though she had Rylynn out of the OR, Dr. G knew this was merely the end of the beginning.

The echo team came in to take another look at the heart, and Dr. G stood next to the technician while the image was obtained. For her it was not so much the conclusion of a case as the continuation of a journey. In the OR, the science and technology of medicine blend into art. Seeing incredibly delicate procedures performed on such tiny hearts makes it easier to understand why a full decade of training is required to get to this point. The medical student scared to put her first stitch into a living person had become the cool, assured surgeon switching out a little girl's heart.

CASE NOTES
PATIENT: ADULT MALE
Date of Surgery: 4/11/2016

Dr. Guleserian occasionally will operate on a congenital heart patient who has grown into adulthood but still needs surgical intervention. These surgeries are generally performed at hospitals other than Children's Medical Center. One took place on April 11, 2016, and it was extraordinary not for the patient or the diagnosis, but for the makeup of the operating room team.

I had an adult congenital heart patient at Clements University Hospital (another UT Southwestern facility). *We were doing the pre-surgical check prior to prepping and draping the patient and I looked up and realized that the entire OR team was made up of women. I was the congenital heart surgeon; Dr. Tracy Geoffrion was my surgical fellow; Sarah Clakely was the OR scrub nurse; Dina Villaraza was the scrub tech; Dawn Bryant was the perfusionist, running the heart-lung bypass machine; Dr. Alicia Wanat was the anesthesiologist; Dr. Elizabeth Brickner was the adult congenital cardiologist who was doing the transesophageal echocardiogram. Nurse, scrub tech, perfusionist, surgeon, surgical fellow, anesthesiologist, anesthesia fellow, cardiologist, cardiology fellow—all women.*

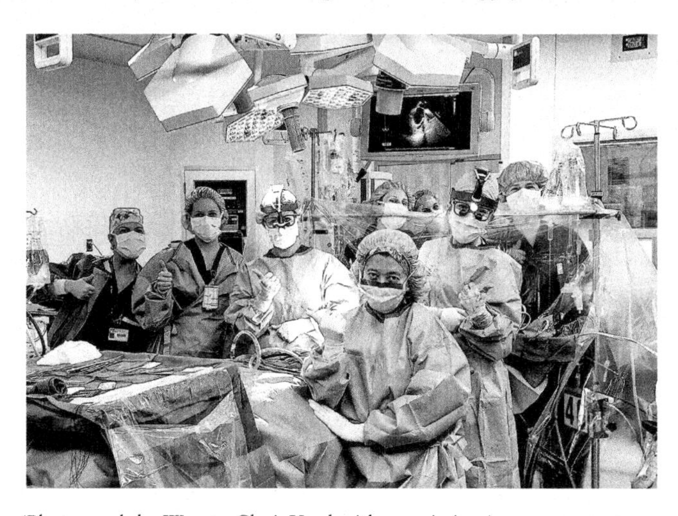

(Photograph by Warren Choi. Used with permission.)

The only male in the room was the patient. After his surgery, I told him the cardiac team that worked on him was all women, and that he'd probably never be the same again.

During surgery, it was all business. However, when it was over, Dr. G allowed herself a moment of proud reflection.

I smiled behind my mask because I was looking around and there was not another guy in the room. The women were doing all the work, as usual. (Just kidding.) I'm very proud that UT Southwestern was the only cardiothoracic surgical program in the country to have four female residents that particular year. That's pretty remarkable when you think about it.

In one way, though, there was nothing unusual about women dominating the room, given the events and people who led Dr. G to this moment.

You have to remember I went to an all-girls school. The class president was a woman, the captain of the field hockey team, lacrosse team, tennis team, basketball team, squash team—all women. The editor of the newspaper was a woman. So, it really didn't strike me as different because that's what I grew up knowing, that nothing was impossible. Women were always doing things. Having women in leadership roles was nothing new to me.

But then I was thrown into the field of cardiothoracic surgery. When I was beginning, I looked around and there were very few female surgical mentors. It doesn't mean that I didn't have mentors, because some of my greatest mentors have been men. Not all of them have been cardiothoracic surgeons. But now, I feel like it's up to me to be a role model for the younger generation coming through. Whether they are women or men doesn't matter—just so I can offer them a different model of a cardiothoracic surgeon.

CHAPTER TWELVE

Fenway Park & Cardiac Karma – Part 3

"Could this day get any better?"

In the euphoria surrounding the Red Sox win that clinched a World Series berth, the offhand suggestion Dr. G made to Andrew before his surgery may have been forgotten by some, but not by everyone. Before the surgeon and her patient could make it from Dallas to Boston, the story had to make it there first. Red Sox president and CEO Larry Lucchino was married to a woman from Dallas who still had family there, including her sister, Stephanie Wilkinson.

"I saw one of the first TV pieces on the story in August on WFAA-TV in Dallas," Stephanie said. "It was the first time I'd heard about Kris or Andrew. When they talked about hoping to go to a Red Sox game at Fenway, I decided to call my sister, Stacey, in Boston and tell her about it. I asked her if she thought the team could help in any way. She said, 'Let me talk to Larry.' I found out more about the story by getting in touch with Michael Rey, the reporter at WFAA, and I passed along everything I found out to Stacey."

Still don't believe in Red Sox karma?

The ball was rolling now. But there were so many questions. Would the Red Sox go along with the whole thing? Was it a good idea to let a kid 21 days out from a heart transplant fly halfway across the country and spend a chill autumn night outdoors at a baseball game?

All of a sudden I was getting countless phone calls from people who wanted to help. One man left a message on my voicemail— "Hi, you don't know me but I want to help. I'm 94 years-old and a huge baseball fan. There aren't many great stories in the news these days but this one, this is a great story. I'd love to help this little boy go to the World Series." This gentleman was crying as he left me that voicemail message and when I was listening to it I started crying, too. It was unbelievable. What an incredibly kind man. And then, out of the blue, I got a page from Larry Lucchino — "How can we help?" And that pretty much sealed the deal.

The plan began to fall into place just as that roulette ball fell into slot 9. Grace Flight of America provided a medical jet fully outfitted with whatever might be needed in case of any emergency, and four pilots donated their time. The Texas Rangers baseball club donated $15,000 for fuel. Press conferences became an almost daily occurrence as the date of the trip approached. Dr. G, Andrew, and his mother Lauri, had a press conference at the airport before they boarded the plane. Texas Rangers officials gave Andrew a bag full of team items. Everybody settled in for the flight to Logan Airport.

When we landed at Logan the team sent over a Red Sox bus to greet us and take us around town. We got on the bus and first we went by the Winsor School, the small, all-girl private school I attended. I told Andrew I'd never be where I was now without the great education I'd gotten there. And he wouldn't be here, either. Not in Boston, anyway.

Then, it was on to Fenway Park. Andrew walked in and just stood there amazed, seeing the Green Monster, the big left field wall, the diamond, Pesky's pole—everything. While we were sitting in the dugout the Red Sox mascot, who's also called the Green Monster, came over and began messing with him. They were having a lot of fun. The phone from the press box to the dugout started ringing and the Monster kept tapping Andrew on the shoulder to answer it. Finally, he did. He sat there for a moment, and then his eyes just got huge. He said, "They want me to throw out the first pitch tonight!" And I was thinking "Could this day get any better?" They took Andrew out on to the field and reporters from all over the country came up and were asking him questions about his heart transplant, and how it felt to be at Fenway. I just stood there, also mesmerized, looking up at all these Boston sportscasters I grew up watching as a kid who were now asking me questions.

Andrew, Lauri, and Dr. G went to the Lucchino house to relax before they were scheduled to return to Fenway for the 7:20 PM game. They watched Andrew's on-field press conference on TV as they were snacking in the kitchen with the Lucchino family. The two of them, surgeon and patient, then walked through the house exploring. In Lucchino's office, they saw a large gold trophy with dozens of miniature flagpoles sprouting up from the base. The two Red Sox fanatics got close enough to realize they were gawking at the 2004 World Series championship trophy.

Stop for just a moment. Consider the odds here. In 1994, when Andrew was born in Odessa, Texas, Dr. G was a surgical intern at Brown University Surgical program in Rhode Island, and the Red Sox finished fourth in their division winning only 54 of 162 games. Ten years later the Red Sox won their first World Series in 86 years, ten-year-old Andrew sat in front of the TV to watch his favorite team win that series, and Dr. G was deeply into her congenital fellowship at Children's Hospital Boston. Another three years, and a surgeon who moved from Boston to Texas transplanted a heart into the body of a young Texas boy, who she then took to Boston for another Red Sox World Series. This stuff only happens in movies.

It was time for the main event at Fenway. The Red Sox PR staff briefed Andrew about the first pitch ceremony—where he'd stand, who would be catching. Dr. G was content to stand on the sideline and watch.

I told him, "Andrew you're going to be awesome. You'll be great on the mound. I'll be right over here watching." And the Red Sox people were saying, "No, Dr. G, you're going out there with him." So now, my fashion sense kicked in. I realized I wasn't wearing enough red. Denise Yates, one of the Children's Medical Center Development Office staff who made the trip with us, took off her big red scarf and gave it to me, and I wrapped it around my neck.

Before we walked out on the field, Andrew asked me if he had to wear his surgical mask and I said no, not for the pitch. He had to wear the mask to keep germs out. I'd faxed all his records to Boston Children's Hospital—just in case. And as soon as I told him he could take it off I thought, "Great, he'll get sick, I'll get fired." Plus, when you've just had open-heart surgery, and your breastbone is cut open and then wired back together, we tell you not to do any heavy lifting or strenuous exercise for at least six weeks. Here this kid was barely three weeks out from a heart transplant and he was going to throw a baseball before a stadium full of people and on national TV. But, you gotta live life.

Top - Andrew Madden throws out the first pitch at game two of the 2007 World Series.
Bottom - Dr. G congratulates Andrew as Red Sox legend Dwight Evans looks on.
(Photos by Lou Curtis, courtesy Children's Medical Center)

James Taylor was singing the National Anthem to a full house and it was dead quiet until he finished. Then the p.a. announcer said, "Ladies and gentlemen. Many of you may have been following the story of 13-year-old Andrew Madden, a Red Sox fan from Odessa, Texas, who recently had a heart transplant at Children's Medical Center in Dallas. Tonight, he's here along with his Boston-bred surgeon, Dr. Kristine Guleserian, from Harvard and Boston University Medical School. To throw out tonight's ceremonial first pitch, please welcome Andrew Madden."

The fans got quiet as he threw the pitch. And when Doug Mirabelli caught it the crowd went crazy cheering for Andrew. It was indescribable. We left the field and we were walking up through the stands to Mr. Lucchino's box and all sorts of Boston fans, big loud tattooed guys from Southie, more polished downtown executives, were high-fiving Andrew... "Way to go Dude! You rock!" And some of the same guys were yelling out to me, "Hey, will you marry me?" I remember turning to one of the ushers and joking with him to write down those guy's names.

Finally, everyone had a chance to sit back in the Lucchino suite and watch some baseball—in between meeting movie stars (Richard Gere) and politicians (assorted Kennedys and Shrivers) who popped in and wanted to talk to the young pitcher and his surgeon. Curt Schilling pitched well for Boston and the Red Sox won 2-1. Andrew wanted to head for the souvenir shop after the game, like any good fan. It was then that Dr. G confessed.

I finally admitted what I'd done in Vegas when I bet on his number. So, I took him to the souvenir shop and told him to get whatever he wanted. At that point it was well after midnight and between meeting people in the suite during the game and chatting with everybody, I realized I hadn't had anything to eat and I was starving. Even though the suite was filled with hot dogs, lobster rolls, everything you could imagine, Mr. Lucchino ordered a pizza after the game, and I asked him if I could have a slice, especially the part with the burnt crust. That's my favorite. His, too.

Then, Charles Steinberg, the Red Sox VP of Public Affairs, came over and asked me whether Andrew would like to meet some of the players. The one he really wanted to meet was Josh Beckett, the pitcher, his hero, a fellow Texan. They took us down to the clubhouse and we met everybody and got pictures with every player. Every Red Sox player came up to Andrew and was high-fiving him, telling him what a great job he did. And they meant it. They were genuinely happy for him. Big Papi—David Oritz, Kyle Snyder, whose father is a cardiothoracic surgeon, Dustin Pedroia, Josh Beckett, all of them. By then most of the players were on the bus because they had to fly to Colorado for game three, and I hadn't seen my favorite player, Mike Lowell. We were about to leave and the last person out of the clubhouse was Mike. He walked up to us, freshly dressed, smokin' hot, right? Andrew's mother took a photo of the three of us.

Two days later while doing the CBS morning show, live on-air, Andrew said he had a present for me and gave me a framed copy of the picture we took with Mike Lowell. He told me, 'I cropped myself out, so it's just you and Mike now.'

* * *

Andrew Madden is now a student at Odessa College, still a big baseball fan with a very special set of memories. He remembers his relationship with Dr. G as something wonderful and lasting.

"We really became friends because we both love baseball so much. All the assurance she gave to me through the whole thing was wonderful."

Andrew's memories of Fenway Park are as vivid in his mind today as they were that moment he took his first step onto the warning track.

"The first time I went on to the field it was a few hours before the game. I saw the Green Monster and I couldn't believe how big it was. I kind of felt at home because I grew up on baseball diamonds and I was finally back on a field. But this was Fenway Park! I still get chills remembering how packed the stands were. When I was out on the mound and the crowd was cheering, you could feel the ground shake."

Looking back, which is the better memory for Andrew: the fact that he has a new heart, or that he threw out the first pitch at a World Series game?

"The first pitch at the World Series wouldn't have been possible without the new heart. But the first pitch has a special place in the heart I have now."

* * *

Andrew's new heart came from 24-year-old Cecilia Solis. She signed a donor card just before she became pregnant. She died of a brain aneurysm ten days after giving birth to her daughter. In addition to the heart she gave Andrew, Cecilia's liver went to a woman on the east coast and her kidneys, pancreas, and lungs went to people in Texas. Cecilia's husband, Alfonso, says he hopes that Andrew always tries to leave every place he goes a little better than he found it.

"He got a second chance at life," Alfonso said. "Most people don't get that opportunity. Make the most of life. It's precious. Don't waste it."

* * *

For Dr. G, the world goes round. Long days turn into nights, surgeries blend with teaching, consults, paperwork, little social life, and the constant pressure of a career spent healing the smallest and sickest. This is a woman who can sew a tiny tube the diameter of a piece of elbow macaroni onto the walnut-sized heart of a newborn. It's an intense life and a hard one. It is not, pardon the expression, for the faint of heart. Hers is the story of a person whose skill you can never fully appreciate until you are in desperate need of it. And then that skill, and the friendship and caring that come with it, are everything.

CHAPTER THIRTEEN

Post-Op

"It's all about teamwork. It's not about an individual—ever."

December 25, 2009

It's Christmas night at the Oristano house. The table is set for three—me, my wife Lynn, and Dr. G. There's a standing rib roast, Yorkshire pudding, sweet potato casserole, English peas, and a Christmas pudding from Fortnum & Mason in London. I was looking forward to handing Dr. G the carving knife and watching her attack the roast as only a surgeon could. Little did we know that a couple of hours before dinner she'd gotten the call that a heart was available for transplant into one of her younger patients. She was going to play Santa for real.

She came to the house, explained the situation, wolfed down a full Christmas dinner in about ten minutes, said thanks, and went off to transplant. Welcome to her life.

June 1, 2016

It didn't take me long to realize that, organic chemistry notwithstanding, I never had what it takes to be a heart surgeon. The knowledge required, the information to keep up with, the skill set, and the stamina to stand at the OR table for four, eight, fourteen hours at a time is beyond most people's ability and endurance. Cardiothoracic surgery is a difficult and demanding profession, and it takes somebody with a special dedication to make it work, for patient and surgeon alike.

What makes Dr. G different is that she is an ordinary person with an extraordinary talent. You might expect the giant ego, the air of superiority to waft from her, but you'd be wrong. I was lucky in that I got to know the person before I knew the surgeon, and so I knew that this project would be both informative and entertaining for me. As I approached the end of my journey through congenital heart surgery, I had a few more questions about her life and career, things I knew it would be difficult for her to talk about but, as with everything else we discussed, she spared no detail.

The first question was quite simple: Is medicine still worth going into as a career?

You know, I'm not sure. I love what I do. I did an arterial switch this morning on this cute little peanut. The kid did great. His parents are so happy. He's going to be a completely normal kid now. That's why I went into congenital heart surgery, so I could make a difference in these kids' lives. As opposed to, with all due respect, an elderly, 90-year-old who has already lived a pretty full life. These kids have their whole lives ahead of them. For me, that's what it's all about.

For her, the mystery of what lies beneath is what continues to call to her.

It's a mentally challenging field. I feel like you spend all those years studying and going to school and learning about it all—not just anatomy and physiology, but how to put it all together. If you like problem-solving, and attention to detail, this field is perfect, because there's a lot of it. There's a lot of, "Hey, wait a minute, that doesn't make sense. Let's really look at this kiddo and gather all the data. Let's figure it out." For me, my biggest fear in life is being bored. So far that hasn't happened yet.

Every career choice involves both the possibility of reward, and the need to sacrifice. Sometimes, the scales tip more one way than the other.

It's a huge personal sacrifice. For some people in this field, family life can be very challenging. I work in a man's world. Because I'm not married, I don't have a wife at home who can do stuff for me. And the training to get to this point takes a really long time and involves a lot of time away from any home life. There are a lot of people in my field who are divorced, or in unhappy marriages, people on their second or third spouses. It's just difficult.

That it's a man's world is no surprise. And while Dr. G is one of a handful of women in her specialty, she always takes note of the women who came before her, who faced adversity and went on to triumph.

When my brother Michael had his TOF surgery as a little kid, he had what's called a Blalock-Taussig shunt. It's named for Dr. Helen Taussig and Dr. Alfred Blalock. Dr. Taussig was a cardiologist who ran the Blue Baby Clinic at Johns Hopkins in Baltimore. Because she had hearing problems, she was not able to fully utilize a stethoscope, which forced her to become a much more "hands on" doctor, doing lots of visual examination and palpation to diagnose the blue babies.

In her clinic work, Dr. Taussig noticed that blue babies whose ductus arteriosus remained open after birth fared better than babies whose ductus closed. She knew of a pediatric surgeon in Boston, Dr. Robert Gross, who had successfully closed a patent ductus arteriosus in a young girl, and she went to see him. She was hoping he might be open to a new idea. Could he possibly develop a procedure for keeping the ductus open after birth, to help keep the newborn heart from becoming overtaxed? Legend has it that Dr. Gross looked at her and said, in his most haughty, Boston voice, "Madam, I am not in the business of creating ductuses, I'm in the business of ligating them." So much for that idea. (Dr. Gross also didn't know that the plural of ductus is actually düctus. It's a noun, fourth declension, masculine.)

Back in Baltimore, Dr. Taussig also knew a surgeon who was right there at Johns Hopkins, Dr. Alfred Blalock who, along with his surgical technician Vivien Thomas, was developing an animal model of pulmonary hypertension. They were redirecting blood from the subclavian artery to the pulmonary artery, essentially creating the shunt she'd imagined. They teamed up and made history in November of 1944 with the first Blalock-Taussig shunt for tetralogy of Fallot. Whenever I do that procedure now, I make sure to call my brother and tell him.

While going through her training, Dr. G and her colleagues were subjected to a regimen that was so long and rigorous it may have weeded out more people than it should have.

When I was training, there was actually a big drop in the number of people who were interested in getting into cardiothoracic surgery. The training period was long, the jobs weren't abundant, the reimbursement wasn't there like it used to be. Thankfully, surgical educators started focusing efforts on cardiothoracic training so that more people would be exposed to, and eventually go into, the specialty.

Finding herself in a profession where you don't begin to reach true success until middle age at least, Dr. G occasionally asks herself a question we all ask: would she do it again?

There are so many things that have happened along the way that were great. I mean, I will go to my grave thinking, "I stood on the pitcher's mound at Fenway Park for the World Series!" Now, I know not everybody is a great sports enthusiast, but you have to know that's one of the most unbelievable things in life to do. I get photographs and letters from families who are just so grateful. Sometimes, it may be what I think is the simplest operation in the world, and those people are the most grateful. I operated on a woman from Costa Rica who had tetralogy of Fallot and needed a pulmonary valve. I got a letter from her saying that she was so thankful. She'd just had a baby, and it wouldn't have been possible without her surgery, and that I'd changed her life. I'm sorry, but I don't know how many years I'd have to work on Wall Street or how many trials I'd have to win as a lawyer to have this experience, to feel like I had made a difference. I'm sure there is some equivalent satisfaction. But when people ask me, "How's the little boy you took to the World Series?" and I say, "He's doing great. He's 22 now," and then I think, "Man, where did the time go?"

Even with a background of extensive education and training, unexpected things come up, and adaptability is key.

One time we had this tiny, very premature baby who presented with a heart defect that none of us had ever seen before. We operated on her, and we thought we had the correct diagnosis, but she ended up dying. And we found out afterward that she had something very unusual that had not been noted on the pre-operative echocardiogram. We all agreed we'd probably never see that one-in-a-million heart defect again. One month later, another premature baby came in with exactly the same diagnosis. Because of the generosity of that first family, allowing us to perform an autopsy on their baby, we were able to save the next little one. And to me, that's what it's all about. Learning from that previous experience to make our team better and better for all those to come.

Despite the time constraints that plague her life in general, Dr. G still has time to dedicate to special projects that allow her to touch lives existing far away from her Dallas hospital base.

I love being involved with The HeartGift Foundation, a non-profit organization that brings children with congenital heart defects from underserved countries to us for heart surgery. These kids come to us from Ghana, Mongolia, Honduras, Haiti, Liberia, Christmas Island, all over. These are children who would otherwise die without heart surgery. While their heart defects may be simple for us to repair, the repairs are life changing for them. These are truly some of the most rewarding cases for me.

What about the next generation? The students, in medical school, nursing school, even high school, who are thinking about careers in cardiothoracic surgery? What does Dr. G tell them?

I tell them to come spend time with me, because they need to see what it's really like. It's all wonderful and glamorous when you go home at five or six o'clock at night. But we don't go home that early. It's wonderful, yes, and glamorous at times, sure. But it's tough.

I have some students who come through here that I mentor and I can just tell they're going to go on to be rock stars in surgery. And then I have some like a young kid I had in the OR the other day. He told me he thought he wanted to go into cardiology, or maybe cardiac surgery. We weren't even halfway done with the surgery he was watching. He just said, "Thanks," and walked out the door. Never heard from him again. He didn't have the surgical personality.

He didn't have what it takes, because what it takes is a fighter. You don't want a lackadaisical heart surgeon.

You want someone who's going to be invested, who's passionate, who'll stomp on the ground a little bit from time to time. The good pediatric heart surgeon is not the one who usually sat in the back of the room and never spoke up or raised their hand. You can never be comfortable. You have to be on your toes all the time. The simplest thing may turn into something else in an instant. You have to be ready for just about anything.

Over the years I spent following Dr. G around, one thing was abundantly clear from the start—it wasn't about her.

It's not about an individual, ever. It's all about teamwork. It's about the common vision and the common goal of really focusing on one patient, and one issue, and one problem, and making sure you get the child through it. Then, you move on to the next one. Whatever you learned from the ones before, good, bad, or otherwise, you take with you.

* * *

Rylynn Riojas is seven, on minimal anti-rejection medication, and living an active, full "Tomboy" life on the family ranch in central Texas.

Gilly, Rylynn and Andrea Riojas at Children's Medical Center
July, 2016
(Photo by Lori Charles Walker)

AFTERWORD

by Lizzie Cochran

The first time I met Dr. Guleserian, all I could think about was not passing out. I was a pre-med student at Columbia University, and Dr. G granted me the opportunity to observe my first surgery. Having read stories about naïve young students collapsing into the sterile field upon witnessing their first incision, I was determined to hold my own in the operating room or, at the very least, remain upright. Luckily that initial incision and the surgery that followed, a repair of a coarctation of the aorta—in an infant so tiny I could barely believe she was old enough to undergo open-heart surgery—all passed without incident. I left the OR with a new sense of wonder at Dr. G's world of pediatric cardiothoracic surgery.

Since observing that first surgery, Dr. G has given me the opportunity to watch her perform three heart transplants. I walked away from that first day with Dr. G, and from each surgery since, certain that I wanted to be a pediatric cardiothoracic surgeon. I couldn't imagine doing anything more meaningful on a daily basis. With one year of medical school down, I still feel that way. Dr. G has not only given me the chance to watch her work, she also provided a constant stream of support as I worked my way through my pre-medical curriculum, my MCATs, and the start of medical school. Who would have guessed that in addition to being an incredible heart surgeon, she is also a terrific cheerleader?

A few days after I shadowed Dr. G for the first time, a sudden pain in my stomach caused me to double over. I slept fitfully that night thinking it must have been something I ate. When I awoke the next morning, the pain was still there, so I went to a walk-in clinic. After explaining my symptoms to the doctor, he instructed me to lie back, pressed down into my abdomen, and quickly released. The pain was intense, and the diagnosis was evident—appendicitis. That afternoon, only three days after observing my first surgery, I underwent my first surgery.

Later that day I received a text from Dr. G that I immediately saved and have kept ever since. "Watching your first surgery and having your first surgery all in one week," she wrote. "Now you know you are meant to be a surgeon."

She can never know how much that simple vote of confidence means to me. I would love nothing more than to be the kind of surgeon that Dr. Guleserian is. She is at the top of her field, a technically excellent surgeon to whom I would entrust my life, or the life of my child, without a second thought. She is kind and compassionate, energetic and optimistic. Every day she sees children and their families who are going through one of the most terrifying and challenging experiences imaginable, and she acts as a beacon to guide them through the darkness that is chronic, life-threatening illness. She works to push her field forward, and advocates for the highest quality of treatment for all patients. She is an incredible mentor to the students she teaches, not to mention a hero and friend to the countless patients who have had the good fortune of calling her their doctor.

"You are meant to be a surgeon."

What an honor that would be.

Lizzie Cochran
UT Southwestern Medical School
Dallas, TX
June, 2016

CPSIA information can be obtained
at www.ICGtesting.com
Printed in the USA
LVOW01s0917010417
529129LV00002BB/2/P